NORTHROP
BLACK WIDOW P-61

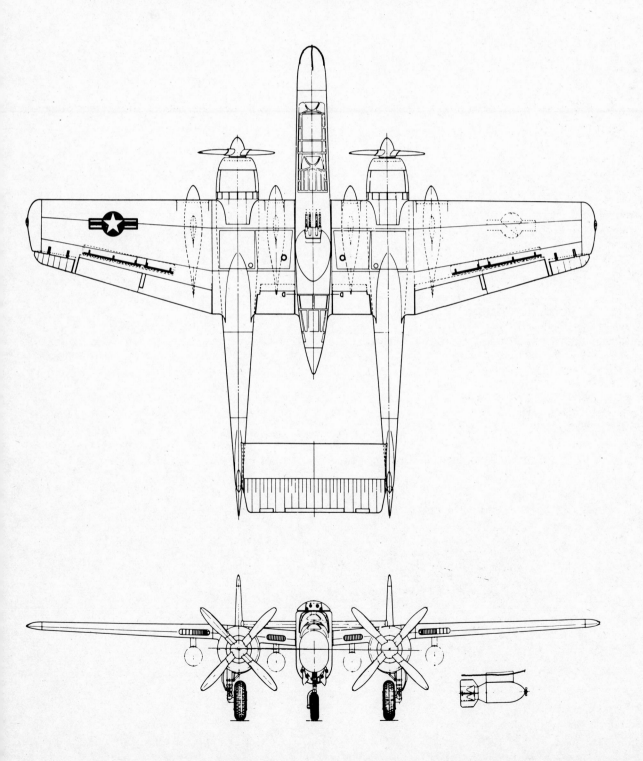

AIRCRAFT MANUAL SERIES

B-26 Martin Marauder
North American B-25 Mitchell Bomber
B-24 Liberator
B-17 Flying Fortress
Lockheed P-38 Lightning
Bell P-39 Airacobra
Curtiss P-40 Warhawk
Republic P-47 Thunderbolt
Northrop P-61 Black Widow
Bell P-63 Kingcobra
Chance Vought F4U Corsair
Grumman F6F Hellcat
Grumman FM2 Wildcat
F-82 Twin Mustang
Lockheed F-80 Shooting Star
Story of the Texan AT-6
Flying Wings of Northrop
Messerschmitt ME-262 Sturmvogel
DeHavilland Mosquito
Supermarine Spitfire
Hawker Hurricane
Ford Trimotor
Curtiss Standard JN4-D Jenny
X-15 Research Airplane

TECHNICAL & REFERENCE MANUALS

Aircraft Detail Design Manual 2nd Ed.
Aircraft Hardware Standards Manual & Engineering Reference
Comprehensive Guide to Airfoil Sections
Handbook of Airfoil Sections for Light Aircraft
Helicopter Design and Data Manual
World War II Intl. Aircraft Recognition Manual
Curtiss OX-5 Aeronautical Engine
J-3 Piper Cub Service Manual

Published in the United States of America
by

AVIATION Publications
A Division of Graphic Communications Center, Inc.

213-217 East Washington Street
Box 357 Appleton, WI 54912-0357
414-733-4483
FAX: 414/733-0676

©Copyright Aviation Publications 1977

ISBN No. 0-87994-025-5

Litho in U.S.A. at Graphic Communications Center
with production by Badger Printing Division
Appleton, Wisconsin 54912

Northrop YP-61, AAC 41-18882, in olive-drab paint, is one of the service-test models.

P-61 SPECIFICATIONS

MODEL	POWER (2)	SPAN	LENGTH	HEIGHT	WING AREA (ft²)	EMPTY WEIGHT (lbs.)	GROSS WEIGHT (lbs.)	TOP SPEED (mph)	STALL SPEED (mph)
XP-61	R-2800-10 @ 2000 hp	66" 0"	48' 11"	14' 2"	664		28872	370	70
YP-61	R-2800-10 @ 2000 hp	66' 0"	48' 11"	14' 2"	664		28830	370	70
P-61A-1, -5	R-2800-10 @ 2000 hp	66' 0"	48' 11"	14' 2"	664		27614	369	70
P-61A-10, -11	R-2800-65 @ 2000 hp	66' 0"	48' 11"	14' 2"	664	22200	27300	362	70
P-61B	R-2800-65 @ 2000 hp	66' 0"	49' 7"	14' 2"			38000	350+	70
P-61C	R-2800-73 @ 2100 hp	66' 0"	49' 7"	14' 2"			40300	350+	70
XP-61D	R-2800-77 @ 2100 hp	66' 0"	48' 11"	14' 2"	664		39708	350+	70
XP-61F	R-2800-73 @ 2100 hp	66' 0"							
XP-61G									
XF-15	R-2800-65 @ 2000 hp	66' 0"	49' 7"	14' 2"			32000	375+	70
XF-15A	R-2800-65 @ 2000 hp	66' 0"	48' 11"	14' 2"	664		32000	375+	70
F-15A	R-2800-73 @ 2100 hp	66' 0"	50' 5"	14' 2"			32175	440	70

DEVELOPMENT OF THE P-61 "BLACK WIDOW"

By Leo J. Kohn

(All photos courtesy of Collect-Air Photos)

At one point in the air defense of the United States, the period being 1946 when the military forces and budgets were drastically reduced, only two fighter squadrons had the responsibility to ward off any possible attack against the mainland. One squadron was equipped with the P-47 *Thunderbolt* for day defense, and the other was a squadron of P-61 night fighters. Such was the high point in the potent but relatively short career of one of the greatest aerial weapons of World War II.

The *Black Widow* pioneered a strange new field of aerial combat in the blackness of night, being the first airplane designed exclusively for night fighting. As the first functional night fighter, it was able to find its enemies in the inky darkness with the aid of radar. It brought to an end night bombing by the enemy on both the European and Pacific fronts, while it was extremely effective in destroying enemy planes, buzz bombs, locomotives, airfields, and depots. By the magic of its radar it was able to effect the rescue of many "lost" Allied aircraft.

The great need for a fast night fighter was repeatedly felt since the beginning of hostilities in Europe, and this was especially brought home after the German night raids on London. At the instigation of the Army Air Corps the basic idea for such a fast night fighter was set down in November, 1940 by Chief Designer John K. Northrop of the aircraft-manufacturing firm bearing his name. As envisioned by Northrop, and supported by the Air Corps, the aircraft would be unique — a totally self-sufficient powerful and heavily armed machine, almost an aerial tank if you will. Impressed with the complete concept, the Army Air Corps signed a formal contract for two experimental airplanes in January, 1941, and the airplanes were designated XP-61.

The first XP-61, AAC 41-19509, reflects the validity of the design in that, except for the natural finish, no obvious external changes were made in subsequent models.

The XP-61, AAC 41-19509, now painted all black. Note the early World War II national insignia with only the white star on a blue disc.

The first XP-61, AAC 41-19509, flew initially on May 26, 1942, but further development and testing delayed its delivery to the Army Air Forces until July, 1943. The airplane included a crew of three carried in a central fuselage pod, or nacelle, mounted between large twin tail booms. This twin-boom layout, reminiscent of the Lockheed P-38, and the odd lines of its fuselage, set it apart from other aircraft in appearance, as did its equipment and tactical employment.

A P-61 at Wakde Island off New Guinea in September, 1944. The P-61 pictured here had a white radome as did some other P-61's, while others had black radomes.

The most unusual feature of the P-61 was the then radically new spoiler-type ailerons in place of the conventional ailerons notched into the trailing edge of the wings. Because of the hazards of night landings for fighters on wartime fields it was necessary to incorporate a new system of controls in the P-61. To broaden the airplane's speed range and yet permit it to operate from small fields, it was necessary to run the full-span landing flaps almost the entire length of the outer wing panels. This left no room for the conventional ailerons and the "spoiler" aileron was developed. The "spoiler" ailerons acted like small "gates" which lifted up out of the top surfaces of the wing to spoil the lift and cause the wing to drop. With this short-field capability the P-61 could take off in a mere 1000 ft., climb out at a rate of 2650 f.p.m., and was able to set down again at a remarkably slow 70 to 80 m.p.h. Its spoilers allowed it to make fast tight turns belying the huge size of the

Northrop P-61B-15-NO, AAF 42-39728. The P-61B generally did not have the top turret, but this particular airplane does.

This view of a P-61A points out why it was so appropriately named *Black Widow*. The top turret is seen locked in the forward firing position.

airplane.

And huge it was, in size more nearly comparable to a medium bomber than a fighter. Its dimensions were greater than those of the Douglas A-20 and it was at least a ton heavier. It was about three times as heavy as a P-51 and almost twice as heavy as a P-47 at combat weight.

The construction of the twin booms and central nacelle was of the all-metal monocoque type, meaning that the metal skin was formed around the bulkheads to form the total structure.

A notable feature was the large quantity of radar and communications equipment it carried, all housed in the central nacelle. Included in this central nacelle was the target-identification radar in the nose, crew positions, and armament. The crew included the single pilot, the gunner amidships, and the radio operator in the rear. The gunner, who controlled the radar, sat behind and above the pilot with his own vantage point.

Early P-61A and late P-61B models carried a remote-controlled four-gun turret atop the fuselage immediately behind the gunner's compartment. These .50-caliber guns, each with 500 rounds available, provided a heavy concentration of fire in a 360-degree azimuth. The turret was under the complete control of the gunner unless he chose to lock it in the forward position and allow the pilot to use the firepower. Likewise, control could be passed over to the radio operator who could swing the turret to the rear and fire off a parting shot should the P-61 overshoot its target. Four 20-mm. cannon were mounted in the belly of the central nacelle, each cannon provided with 200 shells. The cannon and turret offering combined forward firing resulted in a

devastating concentration of fire. The P-61 was designed to accommodate eight 20-mm. cannon and ten .50-caliber guns as absolute armament displacement. It was unexcelled for its armament and it was well suited for interceptor, patrol, fighter, and attack duties.

In its night-fighter role, the airplane carried an all-black glossy finish which effectively concealed it even in the direct beam of a searchlight. This, coupled with the tremendous sting of its guns, earned it the name

A P-61 receives maintenance while a barrage balloon rests on the ground behind it.

Black Widow while yet on the production lines.

It was not until more than two years after its first flight that it entered combat in August, 1944 when it was pitted successfully against robot bombs over southern England. It then saw service in France with the Ninth Air Force and gleaned immediate success as a bomber destroyer. It proved itself capable of a variety of night missions, operating as an intruder as well as an interceptor. "Intruder" missions were usually nighttime nuisance raids by single planes against enemy targets.

Northrop F-15A *Reporter*, AAF 43-8335, is a converted P-61C-1-NO. The black paint has been removed, the nose lengthened and displaying camera ports, and the pilot sits under a bubble canopy.

Black Widow squadrons were active in North Africa as well as in the Mediterranean theater. In the latter part of 1944 and P-61 was deployed to the Pacific theater, and it was particularly successful in stopping sneak night raids by the Japanese. Operating with the Seventh Air Force in the Marianas Islands area, they flew between dusk and dawn to thwart Iwo-Jima-based enemy planes which struck under cover of darkness at the B-29 fields on Guam, Saipan, and Tinian.

Once Iwo Jima was taken by American forces, P-61's continued to defend that bitterly won base. It is reasonable to say that the *Black Widow* demoralized the enemy with its attacks in total darkness directed by its uncanny radar. At the same time this wistful *Widow* was regarded highly by Allied pilots who were lost over the sea at night and found and guided home by her.

Without a doubt the P-61 was an enormous airplane. Span was 66 ft. 0 in. and the total length for most versions was 48 ft. 11 in. Its design gross weight was some 28,500 lbs., yet for all of this it was an extremely docile airplane. With its relatively small span, large chord, and full-span wing flaps it took off and landed so easily, and its spoilers made it more maneuverable than any other Air Forces fighter. Indeed, it could turn inside any other fighter it encountered, while its wing air brakes provided rapid deceleration when maneuvering to fire at a target.

The *Widow* employed the powerful Pratt & Whitney R-2800-10 turbocharged twin-row *Double Wasp* engines rated at 2000 hp each and driving four-blade Curtiss Electric propellers.

Thirteen airplanes were produced after the XP-61's and given over to service-test purposes as the YP-61. These were almost identical to the XP-61.

The first production batch was for 80 P-61A's in blocks numbered 1 through 5, essentially the same as the YP-61 but operating at slightly less gross weight. Only the first 37 out of these 80 had the power turret.

The P-61A-10 and -11 came on the scene as an improved P-61 powered with the R-2800-65, also rated at 2000 hp. The top turret was deleted on all 120 of these P-61A's, and its gross was about 1500 lbs. less than the prototypes.

The P-61B was produced in the largest quantity — 450 in all — and had a vastly greater gross weight. The wing was slightly enlarged and strengthened to take four bomb shackles for either 3200 or 6400-lb. loads of

Northrop P-61B with four ferry tanks.

bombs. In addition to the provision for two external drop tanks on the P-61A, the P-61B could mount a total of four such tanks of either 165 gals. each or 310 gals. each, although the latter combinjtion would have been for extreme conditions. Internal fuel capacity of the P-61B was 640 gals., and a total capacity of 1880 gals. was possible with the large drop tanks. All of this fuel was rarely, if ever, used on any single mission. The original combat radius of 700 to 800 miles could be extended out to better than 1000 miles. The ferrying range was almost tripled, and night tactical bombing was added to its duties. The P-61B also used the R-2800-65 and it operated at a gross weight of 38,000 lbs.

The P-61C of 1945 had turbo-supercharged Pratt & Whitney R-2800-73's of 2100 hp each along with high-efficiency four-blade propellers which provided better climb and performance above 25,000 ft. Some 41 P-61C models were produced, all with the top power turret, and grossing out at 40,300 lbs.

A single P-61A was retrofitted with the R-2800-77 engines and became the XP-61D.

A P-61B was stripped of the gunner's position and its weaponry to provide a camera platform, and this became the XP-61E which was later to become the XF-15. At that time the "F" designation stood for "Photographic."

Still further, a P-61C was revised to some extent to become the XP-61F but details of this version are all but unknown. For post-war purposes an XP-61G was being developed but the end of the war brought cancellation of the contract. Either one of these might have been a rumored special long-range day-fighter version.

The U.S. Navy also is reported to have run tests with a P-61 as the Navy's XF2T-1, but it is not known which model was assigned for this purpose.

A photo-reconnaissance version known as the F-15 *Reporter* was developed from the XP-61E, which was reworked into the XF-15 in 1945, its gross weight reduced to 32,000 lbs. and top speed increased to beyond 375 mph. About the same time a P-61A was modified for photo work, becoming the XF-15A, and its performance worked out at about equal to that of the XF-15.

These modifications were then made to a number of P-61C's which became the F-15A. This version had a length of 50 ft. 5 in. and, with its 2100-hp R-2800-73 engines and gross weight of 32,175 lbs., was able to move out at 440 m.p.h.

During 1947 and 1948, a joint military-civil All-Weather Flying Center operated out of Clinton County Air Force Base at Wilmington, Ohio. This was a combined Air Force, Navy, NACA, and Weather Bureau effort to probe the mysteries of thunderheads, lightning strikes, and other storm-front peculiarities to keep the air forces a jump ahead of the weather. Specially equipped P-61's, brightly painted with red and yellow colors to warn other planes to keep their distance, were fitted with a great many instruments to measure temperatures, pressures, etc.

"Project Thunderstorm" was to learn as much as possible about thunderstorms, to learn what happens to aircraft in extreme turbulence, and to determine how much strain and stress is brought about by severe updrafts and gusts in the heart of a thunderhead. To this end, during the more than one year of this operation, the P-61's took brutal beatings from hail and lightning. Lightning strikes would burn holes in the airplane, make a lot of noise and scare the crew to death, but they would not stop the airplane's flight or its mission. Hailstones could really wreck havoc with the airplane, battering and denting it to an almost unbelievable extent in a matter of seconds.

Orders for more than 2000 P-61 airplanes were placed, but only 706 had been delivered by war's end in August, 1945.

The period from 1947 to 1951 saw the beginning of a radar-weapons force to provide an Intercontinental Air Defense. The initial successor of the P-61 was the North American P-82 *Twin Mustang*. The four-engine jet-powered Curtiss F-87 *Black Hawk* with its powerful radar and heavy armament was to replace the P-61 but budget cutbacks forced cancellation of contracts for the type, and ultimately the *Northrop F-89 Scorpion* filled this slot.

Some P-61's found their way into forest-fire-fighting duties and a few may still be engaged in that work. Trans-World Airlines operated a P-61 during the late forties doing weather research on their own initiative, similar to that of "Project Thunderstorm."

The P-61 was the first true night fighter produced in the United States and saw combat only in the closing months of World War II. It was a vital step in the development of the "weapon system" concept in that its airframe was specifically designed to house high-frequency radar and the necessary armament. As effective and efficient as it was, the P-61, except for the few retained for specific duties, did not remain long in the Air Force inventory. Most all were scrapped with the exception of a few F-15 versions, which were redesig-

A TF-61C, bearing the Trainer-Fighter designation of the post-war Air Force, ultimately became a display for an Air Scout squadron.

nated RF-61C, and these remained in service until 1952. Even during its short service life, the P-61 *Black Widow* far outperformed all other World War II night-fighter aircraft and rewrote the book on that phase of aerial warfare.

One of the last remaining *Black Widows*, P-61C-1-NO, AAF 43-8356, serving in "Project Thunderstorm."

Northrop P-61C-1-NO, AAF 43-8353, on display at the Air Force Museum in Dayton, Ohio.

The publisher would like to express his appreciation to Mr. Ron Gerdes of Sunnyvale, California for his kindness in making available an original copy of the manual. The generosity of Mr. Gerdes will also be appreciated by thousands of airplane fans. Sincere thanks are also due to Mr. Leo J. Kohn for his research in the preparation of this historical sketch. He is also to be thanked for the use of photos from his large private collection.

Publisher

ISBN No. 0-87994-025-5

1. AIRPLANE.

a. GENERAL.

(1) The P-61 series airplane is a twin engine, two boom, midwing monoplane. The primary tactical function of this airplane is the interception and destruction of hostile aircraft during periods of poor visibility or under cover of darkness. The principal overall dimensions are:

P-61A		P-61B
66 feet	Span	66 feet
14 feet 8 inches	Height	14 feet 8 inches
48 feet 11 inches	Length	49 feet 7 inches

(2) Early P-61A and late P-61B airplanes carry as a crew a pilot, a gunner, and a radio operator. The nacelle has compartments to accommodate each member of the crew. The radio operator's compartment is in the aft section of the nacelle and is separated from the other two compartments by turret and radio equipment. Late P-61A and early P-61B airplanes have no provisions for a gunner. The turret installation has been removed.

(3) The pilot and gunner enter their compartments by a door in the nose wheel well. (See figure 2.) The door incorporates a folding ladder held in place by clips. The ladder is stowed from the inside by stepping on the button on top of the rod which folds the ladder. Access to the radio operator's compartment is by way of the flush type door in the underside section of the tail cone. (See figure 3.)

(4) **ARMOR PROTECTION.**—The crew members and ammunition boxes are protected from .30 and .50 caliber machine gun fire by a number of armor plates, bullet-resistant glass plates, and deflector plates. (See figure 67.)

b. FLIGHT CONTROLS.

(1) **TRIM TABS.**—The trim tab controls are located to the left of the pilot.

Note

The elevator incorporates two spring loaded tabs, not controlled by the pilot, which are self-operating at high speeds; they provide boost and reduce control forces.

(a) P-61A AIRPLANES.—The trim tabs are controlled by three wheels in the conventional manner. The inboard wheel controls the rudder tabs; the center wheel controls the elevator tab; the outboard wheel controls the left aileron tab *(See 7, figure 7.)*

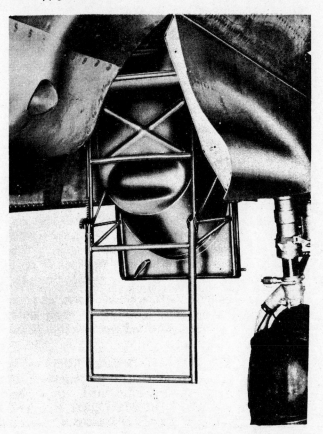

Figure 2 — Pilot's and Gunner's Entrance

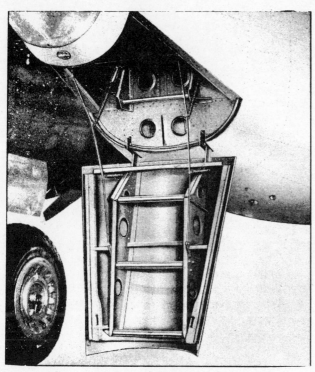

Figure 3 — Radio Operator's Entrance

Note

The right aileron tab acts as a booster and is adjustable on the ground only.

(b) **P-61B AIRPLANES.**—The ailerons are not equipped with trim tabs. The controls on early P-61B airplanes are two conventional type wheels. On late P-61B airplanes a dial knob controls the rudder tabs; the control for the elevator is a wheel aft of the knob. *(See figure 6.)*

(2) **FLAPS.**—The hydraulically operated flaps are controlled by the selector lever on the rail to the left of the pilot. *(See 4, figure 7.)* Full flap deflection is 60°. The flap and landing gear position indicator is in the lower right corner of the instrument panel. *(See 15, figure 17.)* Flap warning lights are located on the left-hand cockpit rail, just forward of the flap control handle, to indicate when the flap up position locks are not engaged. The warning lights are on whenever the lock is open, regardless of the position of the flaps. *(See figure 11.)*

(3) **AILERONS.**—One conventional and two retractable ailerons are installed in each outer wing. They are interconnected and function simultaneously.

(4) **AUTOMATIC PILOT CONTROLS.**—The oil pressure control is located to the right of the pilot, forward of the hydraulic hand pump. *(See 11, figure 8.)* The "AUTOMATIC PILOT MASTER CONTROL" (by-pass valve) is located aft of the hydraulic hand pump, near the floor of the compartment. *(See figure 12.)* The automatic pilot speed

adjustments and caging controls are on the face of the gyro instruments in the panel. *(See figure 14.)*

(5) **FLIGHT CONTROL LOCK.**—Located aft of the pilot's seat, right side, on the floor of the gunner's compartment. Surface controls are locked in NEUTRAL and the throttles are locked in the CLOSED position when the control lock is engaged. *(See figure 15.)*

c. **LANDING GEAR.**—The hydraulically operated tricycle landing gear retracts aft into the crew and engine nacelles. The control (square knob) *(see 2, figure 16)* is located forward and left of the control column. The flap and landing gear position indicator is in the lower right-hand corner of the instrument panel. *(See 15, figure 17.)*

(1) **MAIN GEAR.**—Main gear extension is aided by a bungee system utilizing air and oil which is under compression when the gear is retracted. The gear is held in the UP or DOWN position by mechanically latching, hydraulically releasing locks. There are also provisions for emergency release of the up locks. The P-61B airplanes have an additional emergency down lock release. Refer to section IV, paragraph **6 a.**

(2) **NOSE GEAR.**—The locks which hold the nose gear in the UP or DOWN position are latched and released mechanically. Emergency extension of the gear is also provided. Refer to section IV, paragraph **6 a.**

(3) **BRAKES.**—The ACCUMULATOR system pressure actuates the brakes. The parking brake lever is between the brake pedals. *(See 4, figure 16.)* An emergency air brake is provided for use in the event of hydraulic brake failure. Refer to section IV, paragraph **13.**

(4) **LANDING GEAR WARNING HORN SYSTEM.**—The warning horn will sound if the gear is not down and locked and either throttle is closed to 15″ Hg manifold pressure or less. On P-61A and early P-61B airplanes, the warning horn release is to the left of the pilot below the cockpit rail. *(See 1, figure 7.)* On late P-61B airplanes the release is on the engine control quadrant.

d. **HYDRAULIC SYSTEM.**
(See figures 38 through 41.)

(1) **GENERAL.**—The hydraulic system consists of a main pressure system and an emergency hand pump system. The main pressure system, which includes the automatic pilot, provides pressure for the accumulator system. On P-61A airplanes the wing flaps, landing gear brakes, ejection chute doors, and carburetor air filters operate on the accumulator system. On P-61B airplanes, only the landing gear brakes and ejection chute doors operate on the accumulator system. On P-61A airplanes the oil cooler flaps, carburetor air heat, intercooler doors, and upper and lower cowl flaps

Figure 4

Auxiliary Instruments and Controls

(Right hand, forward cockpit rail.)

1. WATER PRESSURE GAGE

2. AUTOMATIC PILOT OIL PRESSURE GAGE

3. DE-ICING PRESSURE GAGE

4. BOMB-TANK RELEASE

5. RADIO COMPASS

6. AN/APN-1 CONTROLS

7. RADIO COMPASS CONTROLS

Figure 5

Fuel Selector Valve Controls

On P-61B Airplanes with provisions for four droppable fuel tanks)

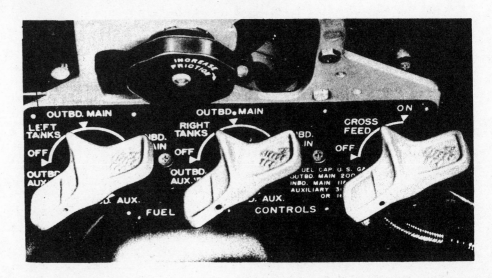

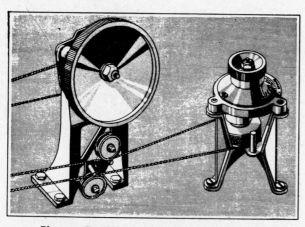

Figure 6—Trim Tab Controls (P-61B)

are controlled by manually operated selector valves. (*See figure 16.*) On the P-61B airplanes the oil cooler flaps and intercooler doors operate automatically from electrically controlled hydraulic valves. Late P-61B airplanes do not have intercooler doors. The automatic control may be overridden by moving the switch in either direction from "AUTOMATIC." Upper and lower cowl flaps are actuated by switches located near oil cooler flap and intercooler flap switches. On all P-61B airplanes the carburetor air heat and carburetor air filter are controlled by switches mounted on the accessory instrument panel, and operated by hydraulic cylinders actuated by solenoid valves. (*See figure 18.*)

(2) HAND PUMP.—A double acting hydraulic hand pump (13) is mounted on the pilot's compartment floor to the right of the control column. By use of the hand pump and hand pump selector valve (12), fluid pressure can be directed to any hydraulically operated unit except the automatic pilot. (*See figure 8.*)

(3) HAND PUMP SELECTOR VALVE.—This valve is operated in conjunction with the hand pump. It has three positions: "NEUTRAL," "SYSTEM," AND "ACCUMULATOR."

(4) PRESSURE GAGES.

(a) P-61A AIRPLANES.—The main hydraulic pressure gage ("SYSTEM") (8) and the "ACCUMULATOR" pressure gage (7) are located forward of the control column below the instrument panel. (*See figure 16.*)

(b) P-61B AIRPLANES.—The main hydraulic pressure gage and the accumulator pressure gage are located on the left side of the engine accessory control panel. (*See figure 18.*)

e. ELECTRICAL SYSTEM.

(1) GENERAL.—The airplane has a 24 volt, direct current system with a ground return.

(2) MAIN SWITCHES.—The main switches are on the pilot's electrical panel which is located to the left of the instrument panel. (*See figure 24.*)

(3) SPARE LAMPS AND SPARE FUSES. One spare lamp box is on the right side of the crew nacelle just aft of the generator control panel; the other spare lamp box is mounted under the table in the radio operator's compartment. (*See 12, figure 56.*) Spare fuses are installed wherever a fuse is used. A spare fuse bag is stowed in the left-hand engine nacelle on the P-61A airplane.

(4) ELECTRIC POWER.—Current is supplied by engine driven generators. A 24-volt battery is installed in each engine nacelle just aft of the gear wheel well. Electric power from a battery cart can be supplied to the system through the external power supply box in the outboard side of the left engine nacelle.

(5) RECEPTACLE FOR SUIT HEATERS. The pilot's and gunner's receptacle is located on the aft bulkhead in the gunner's compartment. (*See 5, figure 63A.*) The radio operator's receptacle is located just below the table shelf on the right wall of the compartment. (*See 14, figure 56.*)

2. POWER PLANT.

a. ENGINES.—The airplane is equipped with two Pratt & Whitney R-2800-10 or R-2800-65 engines, each provided with direct drive superchargers and an auxiliary two-speed blower. Each engine drives a four-blade, constant-speed, full-feathering Curtiss Electric propeller.

b. SPECIFICATIONS.

    (1) FUEL: AN-F-48, Grade 100/130.

    (2) OIL: AN-O-8, Grade 1120.

c. STANDARD FUEL SYSTEM.
    (*See figure 28.*)

(1) FUEL TANK—There are four self-sealing fuel tanks with capacities as follows:

Left outboard tank	205 US	(171 Imp.) gals.
Right outboard tank	205 US	(171 Imp.) gals.
Left inboard tank	115 US	(96 Imp.) gals.
Right inboard tank	115 US	(96 Imp.) gals.
Total	640 US	(534 Imp.) gals.

One tank is located in each inner wing panel and one in each engine nacelle.

(2) BOOSTER PUMPS.—Each fuel tank is equipped with a two-speed electric booster fuel pump. The switches for the pumps are located on the main electrical panel. (*See 6, figure 24.*)

(3) FUEL QUANTITY GAGE.—The fuel quantity gage on P-61A airplanes incorporates a selector control for the tank to be indicated. (*See*

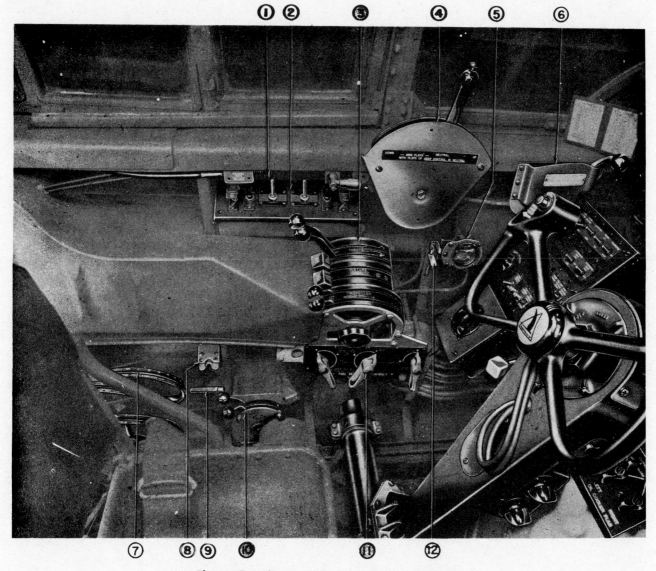

Figure 7 — Pilot's Cockpit — Left Side (P-61A)

1. LANDING GEAR WARNING HORN RELEASE
2. PROPELLER CONTROL PANEL
3. ENGINE CONTROL QUADRANT
4. FLAP CONTROL QUADRANT
5. EMERGENCY AIR BRAKE PRESSURE GAGE
6. EMERGENCY AIR BRAKE CONTROL
7. TRIM TAB CONTROLS
8. EMERGENCY LDG. GEAR RELEASE SUPPORT
9. LDG. GEAR EMERGENCY RELEASE
10. SUPERCHARGER CONTROLS
11. FUEL CONTROL PANEL
12. PEN LIGHT HOLDER

13, figure 17.) The gage contains a red warning light which turns on when about 20% of the fuel remains in the tank in use. There is a button above the dial to test the warning light. On P-61B airplanes the gage consists of four dials and shows the quantity of fuel in each of the four wing tanks. *(See 17, figure 20.)*

(4) WATER INJECTION. *(See figure 29.)*

(a) **DESCRIPTION.**—A water injection system is provided on the later P-61A and P-61B airplanes to obtain war emergency power ratings. This rating represents an increase in power over the military rating of the engine and enables com-bat pilots to obtain a quick burst of speed for emergency operation, either to close in on the enemy or evade him as the case may be. Inasmuch as emergency power represents a strain on the engine, it must be used with discretion. The pilot must treat it as ammunition which he expends un-hesitatingly but only when the occasion demands.

(b) **TANKS.**—Water tanks on the late P-61A and early P-61B airplanes have a capacity of 26 US (22 Imperial) gallons. This is sufficient to permit operation with water injection for ap-proximately 15 minutes. The water tank on the late P-61B airplanes contains 34 US (28 Imperial)

Figure 8 — Pilot's Cockpit — Right Side (P-61A)

1. OXYGEN PRESSURE GAGE
2. RADIO CONTACTOR SUPPORT
3. RECOGNITION LIGHT CONTROL BOX
4. RADIO CONTACTOR SWITCH BOX
5. COMMAND RADIO CONTROL BOX
6. LIAISON RADIO CONTROL BOX
7. RADIO JACK BOX
8. WINDOW LATCH
9. DE-ICER VALVE CONTROL
10. OXYGEN REGULATOR
11. AUTOMATIC PILOT PRESSURE CONTROL
12. HYDRAULIC HAND PUMP SELECTOR VALVE
13. HYDRAULIC HAND PUMP
14. AUTOMATIC PILOT MASTER CONTROL
15. PILOT'S VENTILATOR
16. DETONATOR
17. IDENTIFICATION RADIO CONTROL BOX
18. CHECK OFF LIST HOLDER

gallons, which is sufficient for about 20 minutes operation.

(c) CONTROLS.—The pump switches are automatically actuated when the throttles are full open. Water injection is controlled by the thumb switch on the forward side of the throttle control guide. *(See figure 30.)* The water pressure gage is mounted on the cockpit rail to the right of the instrument panel.

Note

Do not use water injection for take-off. The increase in power is not sufficient to offset the loss of water which should be conserved for more vital use.

d. AUXILIARY FUEL SYSTEM. *(See figure 31.)*

Figure 9— Pilot's Cockpit — Left Side (P-61B)

1. SPARE GUN SIGHT LAMPS
2. PANEL LIGHT
3. LANDING GEAR WARNING HORN RELEASE
4. NIGHT BINOCULAR TRACK
5. PROPELLER CONTROL PANEL
6. ENGINE CONTROL QUADRANT
7. WING FLAP CONTROL QUADRANT
8. WATER INJECTION POWER SWITCH
9. EMERGENCY AIR BRAKE PRESSURE GAGE
10. FLAP UPLOCK WARNING LIGHT

11. IGNITION CONTROL BOX
12. CROSS FEED VALVE CONTROL
13. RIGHT FUEL TANK CONTROL
14. ENGINE CONTROL QUADRANT FRICTION ADJUSTMENT
15. LEFT FUEL TANK CONTROL
16. SUPERCHARGER CONTROL
17. RUDDER TRIM TAB CONTROL
18. LANDING GEAR EMERGENCY RELEASE
19. LANDING GEAR EMERGENCY RELEASE SUPPORT
20. ELEVATOR TRIM TAB CONTROL

Figure 10 — Pilot's Cockpit — Right Side (P-61B)

1. OXYGEN PRESSURE GAGE
2. RECOGNITION LIGHT CONTROL BOX
3. BOMB AND TANK RELEASE CONTROL
4. AN-APN-1 RADIO CONTROL
5. COMMAND RADIO CONTROL BOX
6. AN-APS-13 RADIO CONTROLS
7. LIAISON RADIO CONTROL BOX
8. PANEL LIGHT
9. RADIO JACK BOX
10. FLEXIBLE OXYGEN TUBE
11. DE-ICER VALVE CONTROL
12. OXYGEN REGULATOR

13. CHEMICAL TANK CONTROLS
14. BC-1206 RANGE RECEIVER
15. PILOT'S ENCLOSURE DEFROSTER TUBE
16. DEFROSTER TUBE HOLDER
17. BOMB CONTROLS
18. IDENTIFICATION RADIO CONTROL BOX
19. DESTRUCTOR
20. AUTOMATIC PILOT MASTER CONTROL
21. PILOT'S VENTILATOR
22. HYDRAULIC HAND PUMP
23. HYDRAULIC HAND PUMP SELECTOR VALVE
24. AUTOMATIC PILOT PRESSURE CONTROL

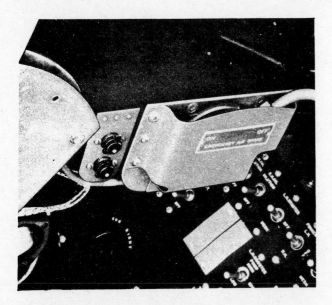

Figure 11—Flap Up—Lock Warning Light

d. AUXILIARY FUEL SYSTEM.

(1) DESCRIPTION.—Late P-61A and early P-61B airplanes have provisions for the installation of two external, pressurized, auxiliary, droppable tanks of 165 US or 310 US gallons each. One tank can be installed beneath each outer wing. With the droppable tanks installed, the total maximum fuel capacity is 1260 US gallons. Late P-61B airplanes are equipped for the installation of an additional external, pressurized, droppable tank on each inner wing. On the late P-61B airplanes droppable tanks of the following capacities can be installed in any combination: 310 US, 165 US gallons. The total maximum fuel capacity of the later P-61B airplanes is 1880 US gallons.

WARNING

Because take-off is critical, operation of late F-61B's with four 310 gallon tanks should not be undertaken except in cases of emergency.

(2) CONTROLS.—On the late P-61A and early P-61B airplanes two fuel selector switches are mounted on the pilot's electrical switch panel.

Figure 12—Automatic Pilot Master Control

(See figure 43.) One switch turns on the fuel from the right droppable tank and the other from the left droppable tank. A push-button type circuit breaker for the fuel selector circuits is located on the generator control panel. On the late P-61B airplanes the fuel controls are incorporated in the fuel selector valves mounted on the throttle quadrant. The fuel selector valves are provided with five positions: outboard main tanks, inboard main tanks, outboard auxiliary tanks, inboard auxiliary tanks, and off. Fuel system management is shown in figure 46.

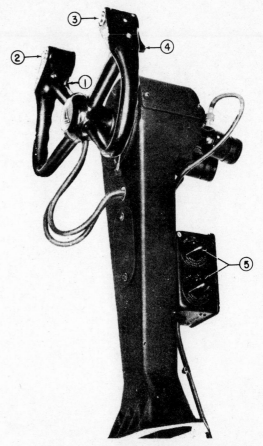

Figure 13—Pilot's Control Column

1. INTERPHONE TRIGGER SWITCH
2. RADIO PUSH BUTTON SWITCH
3. 20-MM CANNON PUSH BUTTON SWITCH
4. 50 CAL. GUN TRIGGER
5. FLUORESCENT LIGHT RHEOSTATS

e. OIL SYSTEM.

(1) OIL TANKS. — A separate oil system is provided for each engine. Early P-61A airplanes having a self-sealing oil tank located in the outer wing panel with a maximum oil capacity of 22 US (18 Imperial) gallons. Late P-61A

Figure 14—Automatic Pilot Control Panel

1. TURN INDICATOR
2. RUDDER TRIM KNOB
3. AILERON TRIM KNOB
4. BANK AND CLIMB INDICATOR
5. ELEVATOR TRIM KNOB
6. SUCTION GAGE
7. CAGING KNOB
8. RUDDER SENSITIVITY CONTROL
9. AILERON SENSITIVITY CONTROL
10. HORIZON ADJUSTING KNOB
11. CAGING KNOB
12. ELEVATOR SENSITIVITY CONTROL

Figure 15—Flight Control Lock

and P-61B airplanes with provisions for droppable fuel tanks have a 42 US (35 Imperial) gallon oil tank in each engine nacelle. (See figure 34.)

(2) COOLING REGULATOR.—Each oil system is provided with an oil cooler installed in the outer wing panel just outboard of the oil tank. The air flow through the cooler is controlled by hydraulically operated air outlet doors in the lower side of the wing. The P-61B airplanes have automatically controlled doors which can also be controlled manually. The position indicator for the doors for the P-61A airplanes is located in the lower right-hand corner of the instrument panel (see 14, figure 17); for the P-61B airplane, the position indicator is in the right-hand corner of the auxiliary panel. (See figure 18.)

Figure 16—Pilot's Cockpit—Lower Front (P-61A)

1. LEFT RUDDER PEDAL ADJUSTMENT
2. LANDING GEAR CONTROL
3. CARBURETOR AIR HEAT CONTROLS
4. PARKING BRAKE
5. ANTI-ICING CONTROL
6. ANTI-ICER FLUID GAGE
7. HYDRAULIC ACCUMULATOR PRESSURE GAGE
8. HYDRAULIC SYSTEM PRESSURE GAGE
9. OIL COOLER FLAP CONTROLS
10. LOWER COWL FLAP CONTROLS
11. UPPER COWL FLAP CONTROL
12. RIGHT RUDDER PEDAL ADJUSTMENT
13. INTER-COOLER CONTROLS

Figure 17 — Pilot's Instrument Panel (P-61A)

1. REMOTE COMPASS
2. AIR SPEED INDICATOR
3. ALTIMETER
4. TURN AND BANK INDICATOR
5. GYRO HORIZON
6. PILOT'S INDICATOR (SPACE FOR)
7. MANIFOLD PRESSURE GAGE
8. PILOT'S METER (SPACE FOR)
9. CLOCK
10. TACHOMETER
11. OIL TEMPERATURE GAGE
12. CYLINDER HEAD TEMP. GAGE
13. FUEL LEVEL GAGE
14. OIL COOLER FLAP INDICATOR
15. WHEEL AND FLAP POS. INDICATOR
16. FUEL PRESSURE GAGE
17. CARB. AIR TEMP. GAGE
18. OIL PRESSURE GAGE
19. CARB. AIR FILTER IND. LIGHT
20. CARB. AIR CLEANER CONTROL
21. AUTO PILOT CONTROL PANEL
22. RATE OF CLIMB INDICATOR

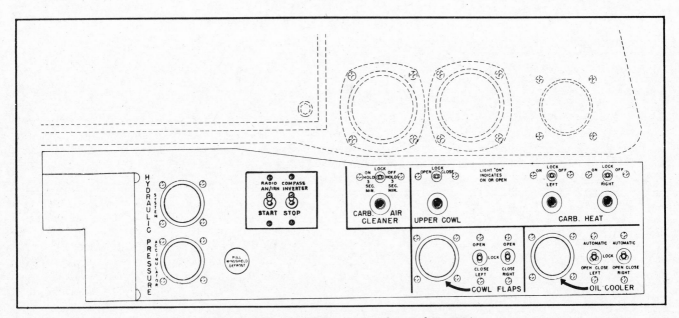

Figure 18 -- Auxiliary Control Panel (P-61B)

Figure 19—Pilot's Cockpit—Front (P-61A)

1. CLEAR VIEW PANEL
2. CORRECTION CARD HOLDER
3. RADIO CONTROL BUTTON
4. PILOT'S GUN SIGHT
5. 20-MM CANNON BUTTON SWITCH
6. CLEAR VIEW PANEL
7. IGNITION CONTROL BOX
8. PILOT'S ELECTRIC SWITCH PANEL

f. **INDUCTION SYSTEM.**—The induction system provides either pre-heated air, filtered air, ram air, or ram air under auxiliary blower pressure for the carburetor under various operating conditions. The air, which becomes heated when the auxiliary blower is in operation, is cooled by ram air at the intercooler.

(1) **CARBURETOR AIR-HEAT CONTROL.**

(a) P-61A AIRPLANES. — The selector control handle is forward of the flight control column. (*See 3, figure 16.*) A dual temperature gage is mounted in the instrument panel. (*See 17, figure 17.*)

(b) P-61B AIRPLANES. — The control switches are on the right side of the engine accessory control panel. A red indicator light indicates when the heat is on. (*See figure 18.*)

(2) **CARBURETOR AIR FILTER CONTROL.**—The filters are controlled by an electric switch (*see 20, figure 17*) located below the instrument panel of the P-61A airplane and on the engine accessory control panel of the P-61B airplane. (*See figure 18.*) A red indicator light at the bottom of the instrument panel indicates when the filters are on. (*See 19, figure 17.*) The filter can be used only with "NEUTRAL" blower.

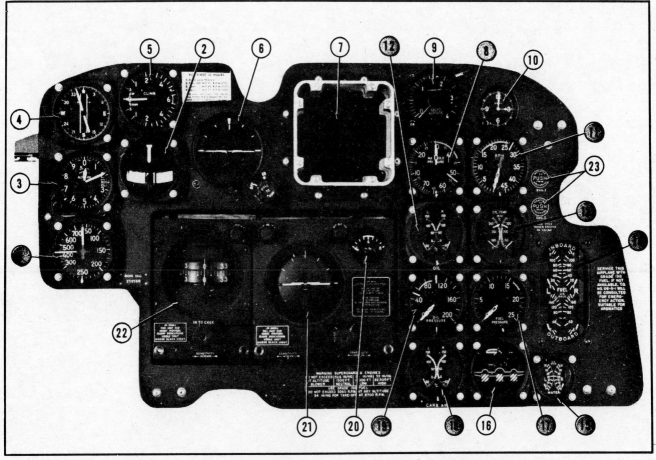

Figure 20 — Pilot's Instrument Panel (P-61B)

1. AIR SPEED INDICATOR
2. TURN AND BANK INDICATOR
3. ALTIMETER
4. RADIO COMPASS
5. RATE OF CLIMB INDICATOR
6. GYRO HORIZON
7. PILOT'S INDICATOR (SPACE FOR)
8. MANIFOLD PRESSURE GAGE

9. RADIO ALTIMETER
10. CLOCK
11. TACHOMETER
12. OIL TEMPERATURE GAGE
13. CYLINDER HEAD TEMP. GAGE
14. FUEL LEVEL GAGE
15. WATER QUANTITY GAGE
16. WHEEL AND FLAP POS. IND.

17. FUEL PRESSURE GAGE
18. CARB. AIR TEMP. GAGE
19. OIL PRESSURE GAGE
20. VACUUM GAGE
21. BANK AND CLIMB GYRO
22. TURN GYRO
23. MANIFOLD PRESSURE GAGE LINES
    PURGE CONTROLS

Figure 21 — Bomb Release Controls
(Intermediate P-61B)

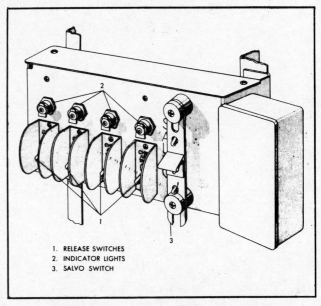

1. RELEASE SWITCHES
2. INDICATOR LIGHTS
3. SALVO SWITCH

Figure 22 — Bomb Release Controls
(Late P-61B)

Figure 23 — Pilot's Cockpit Front (P-61B)

1. CORRECTION CARD HOLDER
2. CLEAR VIEW PANEL
3. PANEL LIGHT
4. PILOT'S GUN SIGHT
5. RUDDER PEDAL
6. IGNITION CONTROL PANEL

7. ELECTRICAL CONTROL PANEL
8. BOMB-TANK RELEASE
9. RUDDER PEDAL
10. LANDING GEAR SELECTOR VALVE CONTROL
11. PROPELLER CONTROL
12. MIXTURE CONTROL

13. THROTTLE CONTROL

Figure 24 –Pilot's Electrical Switch Panel (P-61A)

1. BATTERY SWITCHES
2. OIL DILUTION SWITCHES
3. L.H. STARTER SWITCH
4. PRIMER SWITCH
5. R.H. STARTER SWITCH
6. BOOSTER PUMP SWITCHES
7. PILOT'S GUN SIGHT RHEOSTAT
8. MASTER BATTERY SWITCH
9. L.H. LANDING LIGHT
10. R.H. LANDING LIGHT
11. CAMERA-COMBAT SWITCH
12. PITOT HEATER SWITCH
13. TAIL LIGHT SWITCH
14. WING POSITION LIGHT SWITCH

Figure 25 — Pilot's Electrical Switch Panel (P-61B)

1. BATTERY SWITCHES
2. OIL DILUTION SWITCHES
3. L.H. STARTER SWITCH
4. PRIMER SWITCH
6. BOOSTER PUMP SWITCHES
7. WING POSITION LIGHT SWITCH
8. TAIL POSITION LIGHT SWITCH
9. PITOT HEATER
10. TAXI LIGHT
11. CAMERA-COMBAT SWITCH
12. R.H. LANDING LIGHT
13. L.H. LANDING LIGHT
14. MASTER BATTERY SWITCH
15. PILOT'S GUN SIGHT RHEOSTAT
16. FUEL SELECTOR SWITCHES (LATE P-61A
    AND EARLY P-61B AIRPLANES)

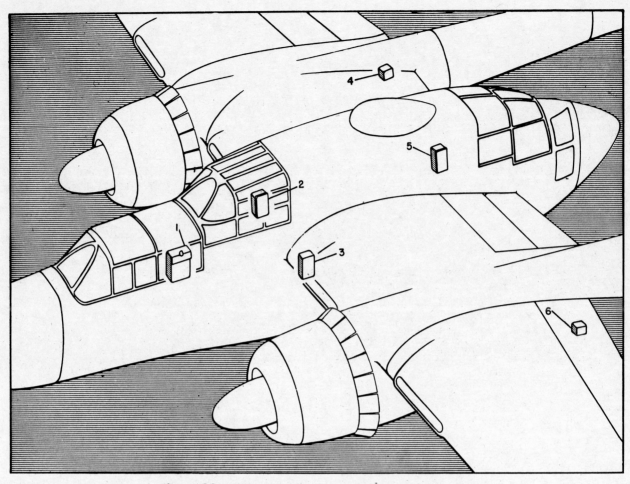

Figure 26 — Fuse and Circuit Breaker Diagram (P-61A)

1. Generator Control Panel

Fuse No.	Title	Amperes
1	Air filter control	2
2	Power receptacle and panel	20
3	Pilot's spotlight, generator panel light, and pilot's oxygen warning light	5
4	Gunner's oxygen warning light and gunner's compartment light	5

2. Right-Hand Junction Box

Fuse No.	Title	Amperes
1	Cannon ejection chute door	10
2	Water injection	15
3	Flap up lock indicator lights	2
4	Machine gun ejection chute door	10
5	Lower ammunition loading lights	2
6	(No fuse installed)	
7	Aft cannon	20
8	Aft cannon	20

3. Left-Hand Junction Box

Fuse No.	Title	Amperes
1	Landing gear warning horn	10
2	Fluorescent lights	10

Fuse No.	Title	Amperes
3	Emergency alarm	5
4	Gunner's suit heat	20
5	Compartment lights and upper ammunition loading light	5
6	(No fuse installed)	
7	Forward cannon	20
8	Forward cannon	20

4. Radio Operator's Junction Box

Fuse No.	Title	Amperes
1	Suit heater	20
2	Extension light and oxygen warning light	2
3	Spot light	2
4	SCR 729 radio	5
5	Power receptacle (early P-61A airplanes only. No fuse installed on later airplanes.)	20
6	SCR 274 radio	50

5. External Power Supply

6. Battery Switch Box

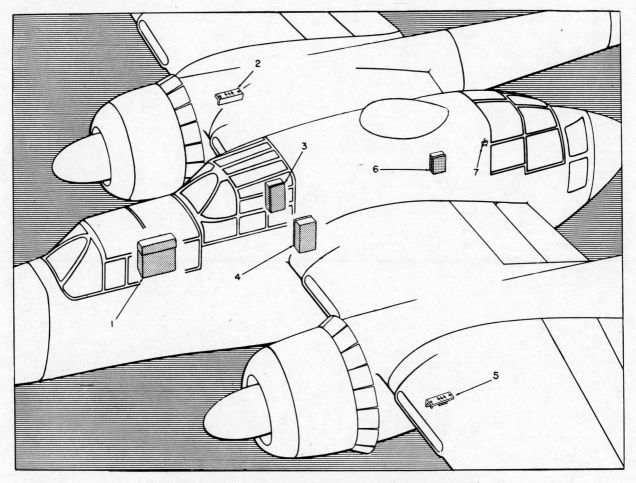

Figure 27 — Fuse and Circuit Breaker Diagram (P-61B)

1. GENERATOR CONTROL PANEL
2. R.H. ENGINE NACELLE CIRCUIT BREAKERS
3. R.H. CREW NACELLE CIRCUIT BREAKER BOX
4. L.H. CREW NACELLE CIRCUIT BREAKER BOX
5. L.H. ENGINE NACELLE CIRCUIT BREAKERS
6. RADIO OPERATOR'S JUNCTION BOX
7. RADIO OPERATOR'S HEATER CIRCUIT BREAKER

(WITH TWO EXCEPTIONS THE P-61B AIRPLANE IS EQUIPPED ENTIRELY WITH CIRCUIT BREAKERS. A FUSE FOR THE SCR-695 RADIO IS LOCATED IN THE RADIO OPERATOR'S JUNCTION BOX AND A FUSE FOR THE SCR-695 TRANSMITTER IS IN THE EXTERNAL POWER SUPPLY BOX.)

(3) AUXILIARY BLOWER.—The supercharger levers are located to the left of the pilot, near the floor. *(See 10, figure 7.)* The indicated positions are "NEUTRAL," "LOW," and "HIGH."

***g.* ENGINE CONTROL QUADRANT.**—Mounted on the engine control quadrant are the throttle, mixture, and propeller governor controls. These controls are designed to make it possible for the pilot to operate them in darkness, by touch alone, through familiarity with the shape of the knob. *(See 3, figure 7.)*

(1) The throttle controls, mounted on the outboard side of the quadrant, are the longest pair of levers and have oval knobs.

(2) The mixture controls, mounted in the center of the quadrant, are the shortest pair of levers and have square knobs.

(3) The propeller governor controls, mounted on the inboard side of the quadrant, are the medium length pair of levers and have round knobs.

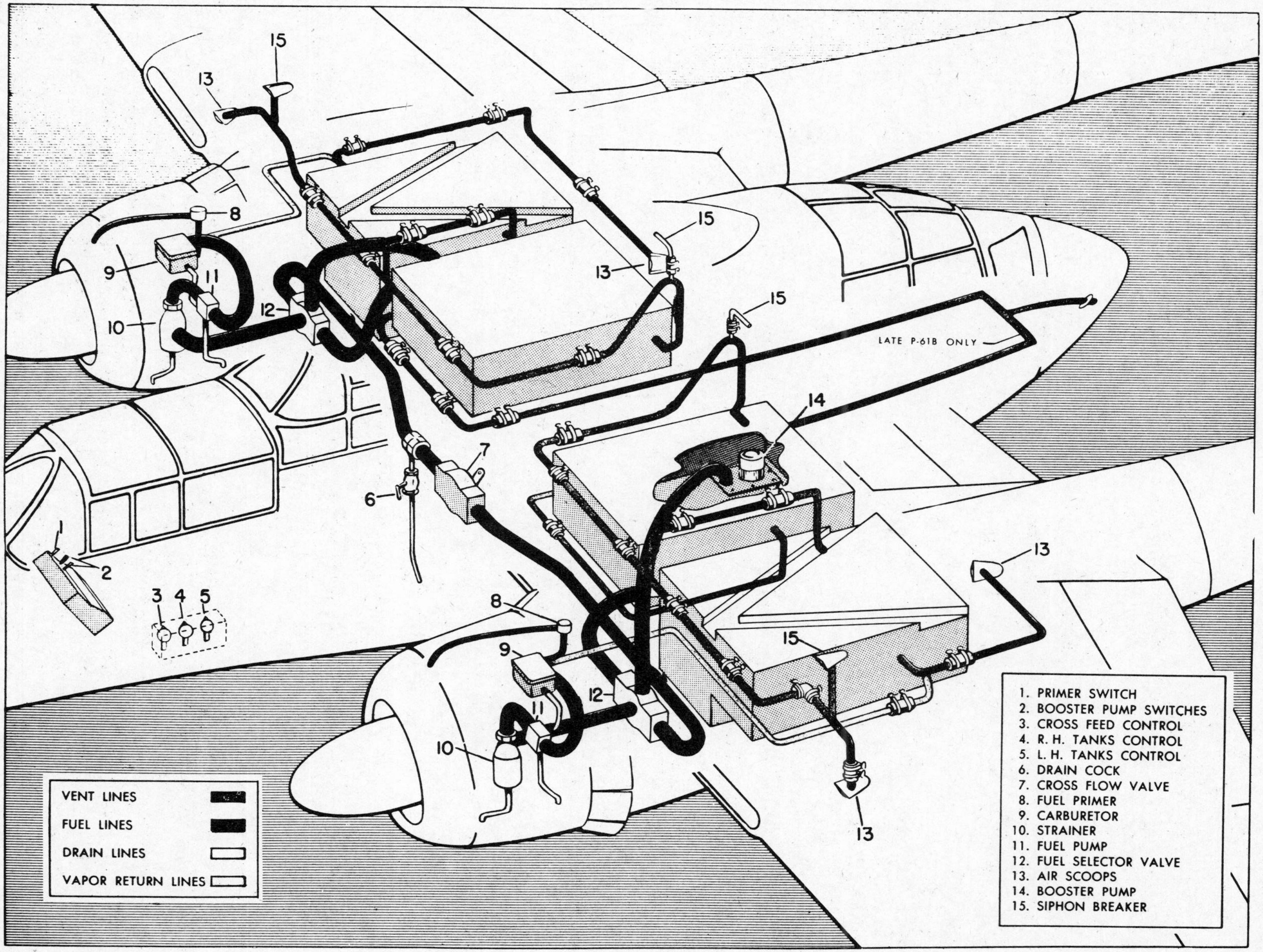

LATE P-61B ONLY

1. PRIMER SWITCH
2. BOOSTER PUMP SWITCHES
3. CROSS FEED CONTROL
4. R. H. TANKS CONTROL
5. L. H. TANKS CONTROL
6. DRAIN COCK
7. CROSS FLOW VALVE
8. FUEL PRIMER
9. CARBURETOR
10. STRAINER
11. FUEL PUMP
12. FUEL SELECTOR VALVE
13. AIR SCOOPS
14. BOOSTER PUMP
15. SIPHON BREAKER

VENT LINES
FUEL LINES
DRAIN LINES
VAPOR RETURN LINES

Figure 28 — Fuel System (Without Drop Tanks)

h. COWL FLAP CONTROLS.

(1) P-61A AIRPLANES.—The upper and lower cowl flaps are hydraulically operated by individual selector levers above the right rudder pedal. *(See 10, 11, figure 16.)*

Figure 30—Water Injection Throttle Controls

(2) P-61B AIRPLANES.—The upper and lower cowl flaps are electrically operated by individual selector switches on the engine accessory control panel. *(See figure 18.)* Cowl flap position indicators are adjacent to the switches.

Note

A red indicator light adjacent to the upper cowl flap switch illuminates when the flaps are open.

Figure 42A—Generator Control Panel (P-61B)

1. AMMETER   2. RECEPTACLE

Note

Pages 20 through 28, including figures 29 and 31 through 41, deleted by revision.

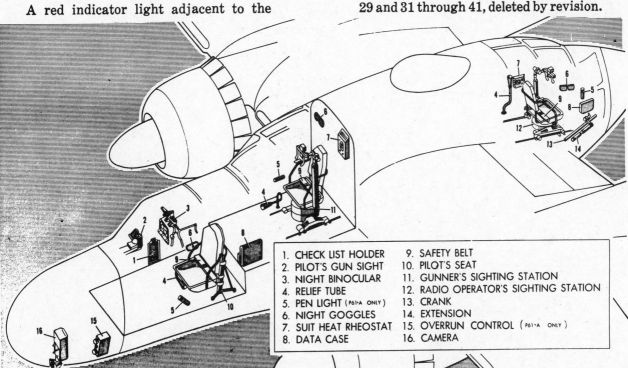

1. CHECK LIST HOLDER	9. SAFETY BELT
2. PILOT'S GUN SIGHT	10. PILOT'S SEAT
3. NIGHT BINOCULAR	11. GUNNER'S SIGHTING STATION
4. RELIEF TUBE	12. RADIO OPERATOR'S SIGHTING STATION
5. PEN LIGHT (P61-A ONLY)	13. CRANK
6. NIGHT GOGGLES	14. EXTENSION
7. SUIT HEAT RHEOSTAT	15. OVERRUN CONTROL (P61-A ONLY)
8. DATA CASE	16. CAMERA

Figure 42—Contents and Arrangement Diagram

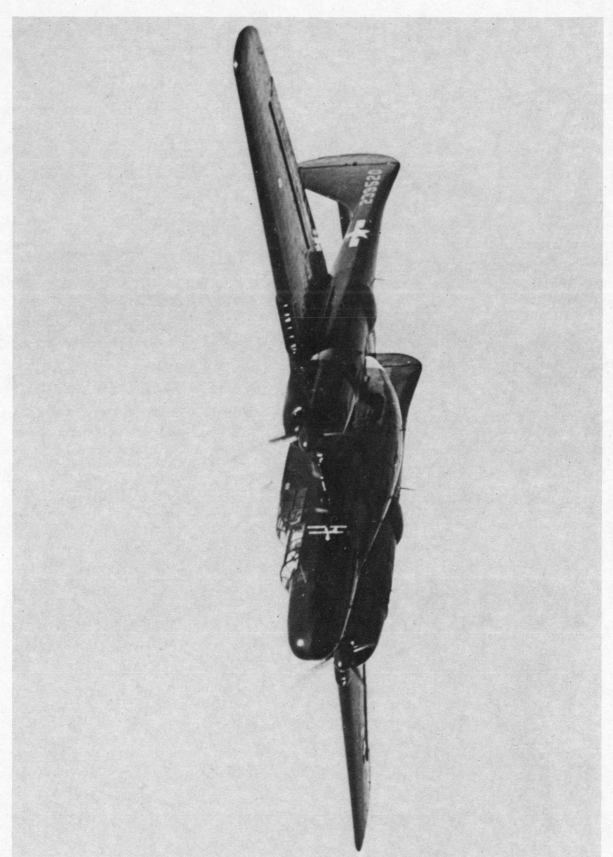

This P-61B-6-NO, AAF 42-39520, does not have the top gun turret.

Section II
PILOT'S OPERATING INSTRUCTIONS

1. FLIGHT RESTRICTIONS.

a. MANEUVERS PROHIBITED.

(1) Outside loops.

(2) Inverted flight.

(3) Spins.

(4) Snap rolls.

(5) Vertical reversement above 250 mph ias.

(6) All acrobatics and steep turns are prohibited when droppable tanks are full. When the tanks are full, restrictions on maximum vertical accelerations are as follows:

Two 165 US gallon tanks, 5.06 g
Two 310 US gallon tanks, 4.00 g
Four 165 US gallon tanks, 4.65 g
Four 310 US gallon tanks, 4.00 g

WARNING

Because take-off is critical, operation of late F-61B's with four 310 gallon tanks should not be undertaken except in cases of emergency.

Note

With droppable tanks empty, no maneuvering restrictions apply other than those of the basic P-61 airplane.

b. AIRSPEED LIMITATIONS.

(1) Maximum allowable indicated airspeed, diving or level flight, 430 mph with flush static (420 mph with pitot static) or .70 Mach. No., whichever is less.

(2) Do not lower flaps FULL DOWN above 175 mph ias.

(3) Do not lower landing gear above 175 mph ias.

(4) Do not operate AUTO PILOT under 140 mph ias.

(5) Maximum diving RPM 3060 (30 sec max).

(6) Emergency landing gear operation—130 mph ias.

(7) Maximum permissible diving speeds (calibrated indicated airspeed, see section III) with tanks installed, full or empty will be the same as for the basic airplane:

Altitude	Calibrated IAS
0 to 10,000 feet	420 mph
10,000 to 20,000 feet	370 mph
20,000 to 30,000 feet	300 mph

(8) Maximum permissible calibrated indicated airspeeds at which empty tanks may be dropped in flight are as follows:

165 US (137 Imperial) gallon tank....350 mph
310 US (258 Imperial) gallon tank....200 mph
(with 36" fins)

(9) Maximum rearward allowable CG for P-61 ferrying is 32% MAC, and for combat is 30% MAC.

c. DO NOT OPERATE LANDING GEAR OR FLAPS WITH AUTO-PILOT ENGAGED.

1A. MINIMUM CREW REQUIREMENTS.

The minimum crew requirements for this airplane is a pilot. Additional crew members as required to accomplish special missions will be added at the discretion of the Commanding Officer.

2. BEFORE ENTERING PILOT'S COMPARTMENT.

a. WEIGHT REPORT: Note weight and C. G.

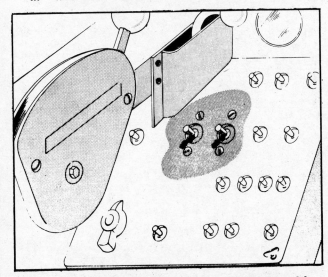

Figure 43 — Fuel Selector Switches for Droppable Tanks (Late P-61A and early P-61B)

Figure 44—Generator Control Panel

1. L. H. GENERATOR AMMETER
2. PANEL LIGHT
3. RECEPTACLE
4. R. H. GENERATOR AMMETER
5. L. H. GENERATOR SWITCH
6. RECOGNITION LIGHTS CIRCUIT BREAKER
7. STARTERS CIRCUIT BREAKER
8. ANTI-ICER CIRCUIT BREAKER
9. L. H. FUEL BOOSTER PUMP CIRCUIT BREAKER
10. R. H. FUEL BOOSTER PUMP CIRCUIT BREAKER
11. PANEL LIGHT RHEOSTAT
12. CANNON RELAY CIRCUIT BREAKER
13. L. H. LANDING LIGHT CIRCUIT BREAKER
14. R. H. LANDING LIGHT CIRCUIT BREAKER
15. COCKPIT HEATER CIRCUIT BREAKER
16. AUXILIARY RADIO CIRCUIT BREAKER
17. R. H. GENERATOR CIRCUIT SWITCH

location. Refer to Weight and Balance Data Handbook (AN 01-1-40) stowed in the pilot's data case.

b. **TAKE-OFF, CLIMB, AND LANDING CHART:** Check (Read **Appendix I.**)

c. **AIRPLANE HEADING:** Into wind.

d. **WHEELS:** Chocked.

e. **PITOT COVER:** Removed.

f. **WING AIR-DUCT COVERS:** Removed.

g. **WING SURFACES:** Free from snow, ice, and frost.

h. **NOSE WHEEL TOWING PIN** (Red cap on): Engaged.

i. **MAIN GEAR BUNGEE:** 750 psi (P-61A), 850 psi (P-61B). A pressure gage is in each main gear wheel well.

j. **NOSE GEAR AIR BOTTLE:** 700 psi. A pressure gage is in the nose gear wheel well.

k. **CHECK OIL & WATER QUANTITIES.**

3. ON ENTERING PILOT'S COMPARTMENT.

a. **STANDARD CHECK FOR ALL FLIGHTS.**

(1) **FLIGHT CONTROL LOCK:** "OFF."

(2) **FLIGHT CONTROLS:** Check for free and correct movement.

(3) **TRIM TABS:** Check operation.

(4) **IGNITION:** "OFF."

(5) **MASTER BATTERY SWITCH:** "OFF." ("ON" if external power is not used; this will be considered an emergency operation.)

(6) **GENERATOR SWITCHES:** Check "ON."

(7) **RUDDER PEDALS:** Adjust for leg length.

(8) **SEAT:** Move for access and adjust for comfort. See section V, paragraph **8 a,** for location of adjustment levers.

(9) **ACCUMULATOR PRESSURE:** 400 psi (minimum). Use hand pump if necessary.

(10) **PARKING BRAKES:** Set.

(11) **FUEL:** Check quantity.

(12) **EMERGENCY AIR BRAKE PRESSURE:** 425-450 psi.

(13) **OXYGEN PRESSURE:** 425 psi.

Figure 45—Propeller Control Panel

1. L. H. PROP. FEATHERING SWITCH
2. L. H. PROP. CIRCUIT BREAKER
3. L. H. PROP. SELECTOR SWITCH
4. R. H. PROP. SELECTOR SWITCH
5. PANEL LIGHT
6. R. H. PROP. CIRCUIT BREAKER
7. R. H. PROP. FEATHERING SWITCH

(14) ANTI-ICING FLUID: 5.75 gallons.

(15) ALL ARMAMENT SWITCHES: "SAFE" and "OFF."

(16) GUNSIGHT: Proper illumination.

(17) COMMUNICATION EQUIPMENT: Check operation.

(18) ALTIMETER: Set for proper reading.

b. SPECIAL CHECK FOR NIGHT FLIGHTS.

(1) LIGHTS: Test operate. Wear night goggles.

Position lights
Recognition lights (10 sec max)
Landing lights (10 sec max)
Taxiing lights (if installed)
Extension and spotlights.

(2) FLUORESCENT LIGHT RHEOSTATS: On and adjusted.

4. FUEL SYSTEM MANAGEMENT.

(See figure 46.)

a. NORMAL OPERATION.—The fuel supply is directed to the engines by the fuel selector valve controls at the left of the pilot. *(See 11, figure 7.)* The forward selector controls the cross flow valve, the middle selector controls the right tanks, and the aft selector controls the left tanks. On late P-61B airplanes the right main and auxiliary tanks are controlled by the middle selector valve and the left main and auxiliary tanks by the aft selector valve. *(See figure 5.)*

WARNING

If sufficient fuel space is not provided in the outboard fuel tanks, fuel return will fill these tanks and cause fuel to flow overboard.

b. EMERGENCY OPERATION.—In an emergency, fuel may be drawn from **any** tank desired for either or both engines.

(1) TWO ENGINE OPERATION FROM ONE TANK.

(a) Turn the fuel selector to the tank which is to supply fuel.

(b) Turn the switch for the fuel booster pump of the selected tank to "HIGH."

(c) Turn the cross-feed valve "ON."

(d) Turn the remaining fuel selector "OFF."

(e) Switch the remaining fuel booster pump switch "OFF."

(2) SINGLE ENGINE OPERATION FROM OPPOSITE FUEL TANK.

(a) Turn the fuel selector to the tank which is to supply fuel.

(b) Place the dead engine mixture control in "IDLE CUT-OFF."

(c) Turn the switch for the fuel booster

pump of the selected tank to "HIGH."

(d) Turn the cross-feed valve "ON."

(e) Turn the remaining fuel booster pump switch "OFF."

(3) TRANSFER OF FUEL FROM ONE TANK TO ANOTHER.

(a) Turn one selector valve to the tank to be drained.

(b) Turn the other selector valve to the tank which is to receive the fuel.

(c) Turn the cross-feed valve "ON."

(d) Turn the booster pump switch for the tank to be emptied to "HIGH"; turn the remaining booster pump switch "OFF."

(e) When fuel transfer is complete, reset the booster pump switches and selector valves for normal operation and turn the cross-feed valve "OFF."

c. CROSS-FEED.—For all normal operations the cross-feed valve should be in the "OFF" position.

d. BOOSTER PUMPS.—The booster pump switches should be kept in the "LOW" or "OFF" position for normal flight. The "HIGH" position should be used during take-off, landing, and high altitude flight.

e. AUXILIARY TANKS.

(1) On airplanes having only the outer wing droppable installations, the auxiliary tank switches must be turned "OFF" when the tanks are empty.

(2) On late P-61B airplanes equipped with inner and outer wing bomb racks, use the fuel from the inboard tanks first when four auxiliary droppable tanks are installed.

WARNING

Because take-off is critical, operation of late F-61B's with four 310 gallon tanks should not be undertaken except in cases of emergency.

(3) It is more economical to use four 165 US (137 imperial) gallon tanks than two 310 US (258 Imperial) gallon tanks. The initial drag is about the same for both installations, but a decrease in both weight and drag is achieved by using the fuel from the inboard auxiliary tanks and dropping them.

CAUTION

Landing with auxiliary tanks full is NOT recommended.

f. TO RELEASE AUXILIARY TANKS FROM AIRPLANE.

(1) LATE P-61A AND EARLY P-61B AIRPLANES.

(a) On the generator control panel, switch "ON" the circuit breaker marked "BOMB CONTROL."

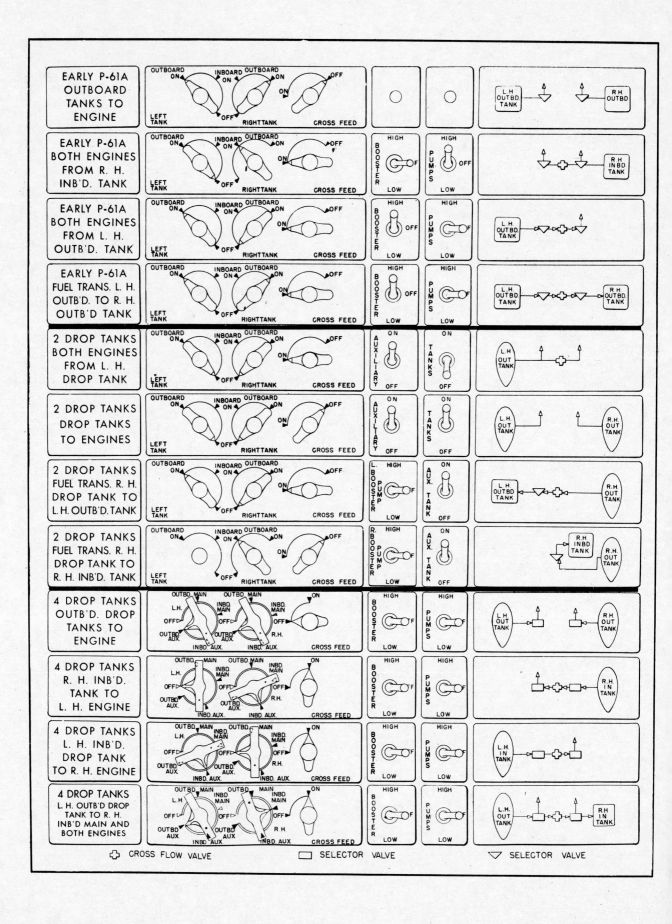

(b) On the bomb selector switch panel, turn the switch corresponding to the desired tank to "BOMBS ARMED."

(c) Press the release button on the control wheel.

(2) INTERMEDIATE P-61B AIRPLANES. Follow the procedure in (1) except, in step *(b)*, place the switch in the safe position.

(3) LATE P-61B AIRPLANES.

(a) On the generator control panel, switch "ON" the "BOMB CONTROL" circuit breaker.

(b) On the bomb selector switch panel, turn the switch corresponding to the desired fuel tank to "TANK." Immediately, as the selector switch is displaced from "OFF," the indicator light for the selected station will go on.

(c) Press the release button on the control wheel. As soon as the tank clears the shackle the indicator light will go out.

(4) TO RELEASE TANKS BY SALVO.— See section V, paragraph **6.**

g. TO TRANSFER FUEL FROM AUXILIARY TANKS TO MAIN TANKS.—Typical control settings are shown in figure 46. It is essential that the booster pumps be "OFF" during the transfer; otherwise fuel will be transferred from the main tank to the auxiliary tank. On airplanes equipped for four auxiliary tanks, when fuel is transferred from one auxiliary tank that tank also supplies fuel to both engines. Hence, the rate of transfer is slow, approximately 350 US (292 Imperial) gallons per hour.

h. WATER INJECTION.—For war emergency power, place the throttles in the extreme forward position and press the power switch "ON." The water pumps are automatically turned on by the throttle or, for ground test, may be turned on by the auxiliary switch. *(See figure 47.)* When the power switch is pressed water pressure should rise to 23 ± 1 psi and, after a brief hesitation, the manifold pressure should rise to approximately 60 inches Hg for operation in auxiliary blower up to war emergency critical altitude.

5. STARTING ENGINES.

Note

Experience indicates that at free air temperatures of $-15°C$ $(5°F)$ or below, pre-heat should be applied to the engines. **If engines have residual heat from a prior run no pre-heat is required.**

a. IGNITION SWITCHES: "OFF."

Figure 47—Water Injection Pressure Switch

b. WATER INJECTION SWITCH: "OFF."

c. PROPELLER: Pull through by hand sixteen blades in direction of normal engine rotation if idle for two hours or more. If cylinders are loaded, remove lower spark plugs and drain fluid.

d. GENERATOR PANEL AND TURRET COMPARTMENT CIRCUIT BREAKERS: Close all except cockpit heaters.

e. GENERATOR SWITCHES: Check "ON."

f. THROTTLE: Open one-fourth.

g. PROPELLER GOVERNOR CONTROLS: Full "INC. RPM."

h. PROPELLER SWITCHES: "AUTOMATIC."

i. AUXILIARY BLOWER: "NEUTRAL."

j. OIL COCLER DOORS: "AUTOMATIC."

k. INTERCOOLER DOORS: "CLOSED."

l. CARBURETOR AIR HEAT: "OFF."

m. CARBURETOR AIR CLEANER: "ON" only if necessary.

n. UPPER AND LOWER COWL FLAPS: "OPEN."

o. FUEL SELECTORS: Outboard tanks.

p. CROSS-FEED: "OFF."

q. MASTER IGNITION SWITCH: "ON."

r. INDIVIDUAL IGNITION SWITCHES: "OFF."

s. MASTER BATTERY SWITCH: "OFF" ("ON" if external power is not used). Leave master battery switch "OFF" until external power has been disconnected.

t. MIXTURE: "IDLE CUT-OFF."

u. STARTER SWITCH: "STARTER." Hold until starter noise reaches highest pitch (20 seconds). Check for fuel pressure indication.

Note

If the engine does not start the first time, allow at least two minutes for the starter to cool before attempting another start.

v. STARTER SWITCH: "MESH." After the propeller has made one complete revolution, turn individual ignition switch to "BOTH."

w. FUEL BOOSTER PUMPS: "HIGH."

x. PRIMER: "ON" as necessary. If the engine is cold and has been exposed to outside temperatures below 15°C (60°F) priming will be necessary. The amount of priming varies from no priming for a warm engine to approximately ten seconds for a cold engine.

y. MIXTURE: "AUTO RICH." To prevent backfiring, movement of the mixture control from "IDLE CUT-OFF" to "AUTO RICH" should occur slightly before disengaging the primer. This should be accomplished in order to allow the carburetor to come up to operating pressures and start functioning in a normal manner.

z. THROTTLE: 800-1200 rpm.

aa. If oil pressure does not register within 30 seconds; stop the engine. When oil pressure registers, proceed with the warm-up.

WARNING

Do not exceed 1200 rpm until oil temperature is above 40°C (104°F).

Note

The starter crank and extension are stowed in the left main gear wheel well in earlier airplanes and in the radio operator's compartment door of later airplanes.

bb. On late P-61B airplanes, press the buttons, labeled "ENG. 1" and "ENG. 2. USE ONLY WHEN ENGINE IS IDLING" to purge the manifold pressure gage lines. The buttons are installed on the right-hand side of the main instrument panel.

Note

Start one engine and check for hydraulic pressure increase to prove that the pump is operating. After flight, always stop the same engine first. Then, partially lower and raise the wing flaps while the other engine is operating. Observe the hydraulic pressure gage for a return of normal pressure after the flaps are returned to the UP position.

cc. In Event of Engine Fire:

(1) Keep the engine turning over with the starter to suck the fire into the engine.

(2) If the fire continues, proceed with the following steps:

(a) MIXTURE CONTROL: "IDLE CUT-OFF."

(b) FUEL SELECTOR VALVE: "OFF."

(c) IGNITION SWITCH: "OFF."

(d) Shut down engine completely.

(e) Do not restart until the engine has been inspected for damage and the cause of fire remedied.

6. ENGINE WARM-UP AND ACCESSORY CHECK.

Note

Do not attempt to warm up engines more quickly by closing the cowl flaps or using carburetor air-heat. Do not exceed 232°C (450°F) cylinder head temperature. Oil pressure may rise as high as 400 psi; high pressure is reduced as soon as oil-inlet temperature is 40°C (104°F).

Note

During ground operations at low temperature when there are indications of carburetor ice, or when engines are rough or back firing occurs, carburetor air heat should be used to correct these conditions. Care should be exercised to avoid carburetor air temperature above 50°C (122°F).

a. THROTTLE: 1000-1200 rpm.

b. GENERATOR SWITCHES: "ON."

c. FUEL BOOSTER PUMPS: "OFF."

d. FUEL PRESSURE: Within limits.

e. ENGINE INSTRUMENTS: Check operation.

f. COWL FLAPS: Check operation.

g. INTERCOOLER DOORS: Check operation.

h. OIL COOLER DOORS: Check operation.

i. WING FLAPS: Check operation.

j. DE-ICER PRESSURE: 8.5 psi.

k. DE-ICER BOOTS: Check operation.

l. AMMETERS: Check.

m. RADIO: Check operation.

7. SCRAMBLE TAKE-OFF.

Note

While taxiing, dilute the oil if fluctuation is observed.

a. MINIMUM VALUES FOR TAKE-OFF.

(1) OIL TEMPERATURE: Within limits.

(2) OIL PRESSURE: Within limits.

(3) FUEL PRESSURE: Within limits.

(4) CYLINDER HEAD TEMPERATURE: Within limits.

b. POSITIONING OF CONTROLS.

(1) FUEL BOOSTER PUMP SWITCHES: "HIGH."

(2) WING FLAPS: 20° recommended if time permits.

(3) THROTTLES: Open gradually.

8. ENGINE AND ACCESSORY OPERATING GROUND TEST.

WARNING

Cowl flaps must be kept open for all ground operations.

a. After oil-in temperature and cylinder head temperature is within limits, make the following checks:

(1) MAGNETO CHECK.

(a) **CONTROL SETTINGS.**

1. **PROPELLER GOVERNOR CONTROLS:** Full "INC. RPM."

2. **THROTTLE:** 30 in. Hg. (2000-2100 rpm).

3. **OIL COOLER DOORS:** As desired (P-61A), "AUTOMATIC" (P-61B).

(b) Switch each magneto from "BOTH" to "LEFT" and from "BOTH" to "RIGHT." Allow a few seconds while at "BOTH" for the engine to pick up speed. Normal drop off is 25 rpm and MUST NEVER exceed 50 rpm.

Note

Freedom from engine vibration is a good indication of proper functioning of the engine, particularly of the ignition system.

If there is an excessive drop in rpm or uneven engine operation, make a quick check at 33 in. Hg.

CAUTION

Continued running at 25 to 30 in. Hg or above on one magneto will foul the plugs and increase fuel consumption.

(2) ENGINE RUN-UP CHECK.—Run engine up to 2000 rpm and check readings for the following items:

(a) **OIL PRESSURE:** Within limits. Oil pressure varies with rpm; it may drop as low as 25 psi when idling, and rise as high as 100 psi at take-off.

(b) **OIL TEMPERATURE:** Within limits.

(c) **FUEL PRESSURE:** Within limits.

(d) **VACUUM:** 3.75-4.25 in. Hg.

(3) AUXILIARY BLOWER CHECK.

(a) Run engine at 1200-1400 rpm to maintain an oil pressure of at least 40 psi. Keep propeller controls in "INC. RPM."

(b) Shift the auxiliary blower from "NEUTRAL" to "LOW" without hesitation between positions. Then, after 30 seconds, shift to "HIGH" without hesitation. (See 10, figure 7.)

Note

If more than one complete cycle of shifting is desired, operate the engine at 1000 rpm or less for two minutes to permit heat generated during the shift to become dissipated from the clutches.

(c) Indications of selector valve and clutch operation during shifts will appear in very slight changes in engine oil pressure and in engine speed when the propeller is not governing. Near sea level there will be no change in manifold pressure but it may be possible to detect the whir of the auxiliary stage impeller and gears as they come up to speed.

Note

Cooling of the cylinder heads and barrels and ignition system harness is usually insufficient while on the ground for continued running above 1400-1500 rpm. Avoid prolonged running at high powers during ground operation. Do not exceed 232°C (450°F) cylinder head temperature.

(4) PROPELLER CHECK.—Supplementary to routine check made by ground crew.

(a) See that the propeller controls are in the "INC. RPM" position.

(b) Open throttle to 2000 rpm.

(c) Pull propeller controls back towards "DEC. RPM" until a reduction in engine speed is observed.

(d) Return propeller governor control to the "INC. RPM" position, noting that the original rpm is resumed.

(5) AUTOMATIC PILOT GROUND TEST. (See figure 14.)

(a) Vacuum (6) should be 3.75 to 4.25 in. Hg.

(b) Check the bank-climb gyro (4), uncaged.

(c) Check and set the turn gyro (1).

(d) Set rudder follow-up card to match turn gyro card; aileron follow-up index to match

bank index; elevator follow-up index to match elevator alignment index.

(e) Open sensitivity speed controls (8, 9, and 12) to a setting of three. Turn on the automatic pilot and check its operation by turning each control knob.

Note

If rapid oscillation of a control results, reduce sensitivity until action ceases.

(f) Auto pilot oil pressure should be 140 psi ± 5.

(g) Bleed auto pilot if controls are "spongy."

1. Turn each of the three control knobs (2, 3, and 5) past the control surface limits.

2. Let them remain in this position for three minutes.

3. Repeat operation with controls completely reversed.

Note

In order to bleed the system, it is not necessary to overpower the auto pilot. However, if this has been done and the controls are moved too far from automatic control position, they will not return when released. Manual movement of the controls toward neutral will be necessary to return them within range of automatic control.

(6) WATER INJECTION.

(a) Adjust the engine speed to 2000 rpm with auxiliary low blower and mixture in "AUTO-RICH."

(b) Press the water pump test switch and power switch. *(See figure 47.)* The water pressure should increase to 23 ± 1 psi.

(c) The engine should hesitate momentarily, then run smoothly with an increase of two to four in. Hg manifold pressure.

9. TAXIING.

a. Release the parking brakes.

b. Rolling motion is an absolute necessaity before the nose wheel will castor. Changing direction may be accomplished by differential braking, rudder action, or differential engine power or a combination of the three. Do not permit the inside wheel to stop rolling. The slower the rolling speed, the greater the turning ability of the airplane. The nose wheel maximum turning angle is 50°.

c. Avoid unnecessary use of brakes while taxiing. In any case, the brakes should not be allowed to drag.

d. Taxi with flaps "UP."

Note

On the P-61A airplane the brakes lose their effectiveness when the flaps are operating.

10. TAKE-OFF.

WARNING

The 20-mm cannon must not be charged until all pre-flight activities have been concluded, the pilot and crew members have entered their compartments, and the airplane is ready to take-off. This is a safety measure designed to protect personnel and property from accidental firing of the cannon while the airplane is on the ground.

a. **PRIOR TO TAKE-OFF.**

(1) AUTOMATIC PILOT: "OFF."

(2) TURRET GUNS: Stowed. Forward and at 0° elevation.

(3) COCKPIT HEATERS: "OFF."

(4) BATTERY AND GENERATOR SWITCHES: "ON."

(5) SURFACE CONTROLS: Free movement. Look at control surfaces to assure proper and full movement.

(6) AILERON AND RUDDER TRIM TABS: Zero. Set elevator tab for load, as desired.

(7) ENTRANCE HATCHES: Closed and locked.

(8) DE-ICER: "OFF."

(9) ANTI-ICER: "OFF."

(10) FUEL BOOSTER PUMPS: "HIGH."

(11) FUEL PRESSURE: Within limits.

(12) FUEL SELECTOR VALVES: Outboard tanks.

(13) CROSS FEED: "OFF."

(14) FUEL SUPPLY: Check quantity.

(15) PROPELLER SELECTOR SWITCHES: "AUTOMATIC."

(16) PROPELLER GOVERNOR CONTROLS: Full "INC. RPM" (2700 rpm).

(17) MIXTURE: "AUTO RICH."

(18) AUXILIARY BLOWER: "NEUTRAL."

(19) OIL COOLER FLAPS: As desired (P-61A) "AUTOMATIC" (P-61B). For P-61A airplanes normal operation, one-quarter to one-half open is recommended.

(20) CARBURETOR AIR HEAT: "COLD."

(21) CARBURETOR AIR CLEANER: "ON" only when necessary. Never on take-off.

(22) INTERCOOLER DOORS: "CLOSED" (P-61A), (if installed).

(23) WING FLAPS: As desired. Neutral to one-third down; depending on length of runway and load.

CAUTION

Set wing flaps from retracted position prior to take-off.

(24) EMERGENCY HAND PUMP SELECTOR: "NEUTRAL."

(25) UPPER COWL FLAPS: "CLOSED."

b. **TAKE-OFF INSTRUMENT READINGS.**

(1) OIL TEMPERATURE: Within limits.

(2) OIL PRESSURE: Within limits.

(3) CYLINDER HEAD TEMPERATURE: Within limits.

Note

Cylinder head temperature will not respond immediately to changes in cowl flap settings. A lapse of a minute or *more* should be expected before a large change in temperature is noted.

(4) HYDRAULIC AND ACCUMULATOR PRESSURE: 800-1100 psi.

(5) RPM: 2700.

(6) MANIFOLD PRESSURE: 54 in. Hg (5 min. max.).

c. TAKE-OFF TECHNIQUE.—At normal gross weight, the best take-off speed is 100-110 mph. The best take-off over an obstacle is made by holding neutral elevator during ground run until take-off speed is attained.

11. ENGINE FAILURE DURING TAKE-OFF.

The pilot must quickly determine whether or not sufficient flying speed has been attained for single engine flight. This will vary with the gross weight at the time of engine failure. Minimum safe IAS for single engine operation is as follows for gross weights as indicated:

Gross Weight	IAS (mph)
27,500	120
31,000	130
37,000	140

a. **IF SUFFICIENT FLYING SPEED HAS BEEN ATTAINED FOR SINGLE ENGINE OPERATION:**

(1) LANDING GEAR: "UP."

(2) PROPELLER: Feather.

(3) MIXTURE CONTROL (Dead engine): "IDLE CUT-OFF."

(4) FLAPS: "UP" when an altitude of 500 ft. has been attained.

(5) AUXILIARY TANKS: Release if conditions permit.

(6) AIRSPEED: Above stalling.

(7) RUDDER TRIM TAB: Adjust for directional control.

(8) WING ATTITUDE: Level.

(9) TURNS: Do not turn until trim is established.

Note

The airplane has a high acceleration just after leaving the ground. When in the air, it has exceptionally fine single engine performance.

b. **EMERGENCY LANDING AFTER ENGINE FAILURE AT TAKE-OFF.**

(1) Refer to section IV, paragraph 1 d, for single engine landing procedure.

(2) TWO ENGINE FAILURE. — A flying speed of 90 mph ias should be maintained with flaps down to provide sufficient control for landing.

12. CLIMB.

The speed for best rate of climb is approximately 160 mph ias. During climbs, cruising, and maneuvers the engine speed should be regulated by the propeller governor controls; the propeller control switches should be in the "AUTOMATIC" position.

a. LANDING GEAR: "UP."

b. WING FLAPS: "UP" after altitude of 500 ft. is attained.

c. LOWER COWL FLAPS: As desired.

d. INTERCOOLER DOORS: "CLOSED." Unless carburetor air temperature exceeds 45°C (113°F).

e. CARBURETOR AIR-HEAT: As required.

CAUTION

Carburetor air-heat is not used when the auxiliary blower is engaged.

f. CLIMB CONDITIONS: Refer Take-Off, Climb, and Landing Chart, Appendix I.

Note

When operating with water injection, full throttle may be used up to 54°C (130°F) carburetor air temperature with the reduction in manifold pressure which will automatically accompany the increased carburetor air temperature. It is unsafe to operate above 54°C (130°F). If this temperature is exceeded, the throttle should be pulled back immediately.

g. TEMPERATURE REGULATION.

(1) A tendency for the carburetor air to exceed 43°C, indicated, when operating in auxiliary blower can be counteracted by increasing cooling air flow through the intercoolers, reducing engine speed, or by shifting to a lower ratio.

(2) A tendency for the oil to overheat can be checked more quickly by reducing the engine speed than by throttling alone.

13. GENERAL FLYING CHARACTERISTICS.

WARNING

If sufficient fuel space is not provided in the outboard fuel tanks, fuel return will fill these tanks and cause fuel to flow overboard.

a. MAXIMUM PERFORMANCE.

(1) The maximum performance of the airplane can be obtained only by operating at the limiting conditions in every factor. Weight should be kept at a minimum for the particular mission and the pilot must be familiar with the handling characteristics at maximum performance.

(2) Pilots should not hesitate, in order to obtain maximum performance, to operate at 260°C cylinder head temperature, 100°C oil temperature, and 45°C indicated carburetor air temperature. (*See figure 68.*) All cowl and intercooler flaps should be kept fully closed and oil cooler flaps should be just cracked open as long as the above maximum temperatures are not exceeded. The preceding comments apply to emergency conditions, and not to everday flying.

(3) Slightly higher level-flight speeds are obtained when operating the engines at 2550 rpm, rather than 2700 rpm, at full throttle above the high-blower normal-rated-power critical altitude. It is believed that this is due to a decrease in propeller efficiency, caused by the higher tip speeds, which more than offsets the slight increase in engine power output resulting from operation at 2700 rpm. Therefore, it is recommended that 2550 rpm at full throttle operation be used for high-speed flight for all altitudes above the high-blower

normal-rated-power critical altitude (approximately 23,000 feet).

b. CHANGING POWER CONDITIONS DURING FLIGHT.

(1) TO INCREASE POWER UP TO MILITARY POWER.

(*a*) Adjust mixture control to "AUTO RICH" if more than cruising power is desired.

(*b*) Adjust propeller control to obtain the desired rpm.

(*c*) Adjust throttle control to obtain the desired manifold pressure.

(2) TO INCREASE FROM MILITARY POWER

(*a*) Engage the water pump switch with the throttle.

(*b*) Press the power switch.

(3) TO DECREASE POWER.

(*a*) Adjust the throttle control to obtain the desired manifold pressure.

(*b*) Adjust the propeller control to obtain the desired rpm.

(*c*) Readjust the throttle controls if necessary.

(*d*) Adjust the mixture controls to the desired position.

c. WATER INJECTION.—Push the throttles fully forward to engage the water pump switches. Then, when the power switch is pressed the water pressure should rise and, after a brief hesitation, the manifold pressure will rise to 58-60 inches Hg.

d. AUXILIARY SUPERCHARGER (BLOWER).

(1) The engine operates in any one of the blower ratios ("NEUTRAL," "LOW," or "HIGH") essentially as a single speed, single state engine. Maximum performance will be obtained by remaining in one blower ratio at full throttle until manifold pressure is three or four in. Hg lower than the value which will give the desired power. Then shift to the next higher blower ratio by moving the control levers **without hesitation** to the new position.

f. COLD WEATHER OPERATION.

(1) CARBURETOR ICING.

(a) When the carburetor air temperature is between −5°C to 15°C in an atmosphere of high humidity or free moisture, carburetor icing is apt to occur. Under such atmospheric conditions, a carburetor air temperature between 15° to 40°C should be maintained. It is good practice to use carburetor heat for one or two minutes every half hour during flight if carburetor icing is suspected.

Note

The carburetor air temperature is affected by the Carburetor Heat Controls only in "NEUTRAL" blower.

(2) EQUIPMENT.—Operate turret frequently, but not continuously, during flight to prevent sluggishness due to cold.

g. AUTOMATIC PILOT OPERATION.

(1) SENSITIVITY CONTROL SETTING.—Best setting of these dials will vary but the following settings are recommended:

	Early P-61A	Late P-61A & P-61B
Rudder	2½	Just below "AVERAGE"
Elevator	3	"AVERAGE"
Aileron	3	"AVERAGE"

CAUTION

Turning any sensitivity control to zero turns off automatic control of that surface and locks the hydraulic surface control in whatever position it happens to be. Very low sensitivities are not recommended for flight in rough air since control response may be too slow for proper recovery from disturbance.

(2) ENGAGING THE AUTOMATIC PILOT IN FLIGHT.—Turn on the automatic pilot by slowly moving the ON-OFF lever *(see figure 12)* to the "ON" position and then engaging the master (by-pass) valve *(see 11, figure 8).* (Reverse the procedure when disengaging the automatic pilot.) By holding the controls, the pilot can feel the automatic pilot taking over.

14. STALLS.

a. APPROXIMATE STALLING SPEEDS.

(1) FLAPS UP. POWER OFF: 110 mph ias.

(2) FLAPS UP, CRUISING POWER 30" HG 2200 RPM: 100 mph ias.

(3) FLAPS AND GEAR FULL DOWN, NORMAL RATED POWER: 70 mph ias.

(4) FLAPS AND GEAR DOWN, POWER OFF: 85 mph ias.

Note

Approximate stalling speeds given are pilot's indicated airspeed for airplanes with flush static installation. Indicated stalling speeds for airplanes with static source in pitot head will be slightly lower.

b. CHARACTERISTICS UNDER VARIOUS CONDITIONS.

(1) In stalls occurring with one engine inoperative, rudder forces to compensate for yaw are high, requiring 90 to 100 per cent full rudder deflection.

(2) No aileron deflection is necessary to hold the ship level laterally at cruising power. At military power, five to ten per cent aileron deflection is required. With gear and flaps down, 75 to 90 per cent aileron deflection is necessary.

c. CHARACTERISTICS AT APPROACH TO STALL AND AFTER STALL.

(1) Ample warning of an impending stall occurs in the form of strong tail buffeting.

(2) Up to and in the stall, elevator, rudder, aileron controls remain effective. No deflection of the controls is necessary to prevent roll in the stall once the controls have been set to produce a stall.

Note

Because this airplane has such unusually excellent stall characteristics, it is recommended that pilots investigate normal stalls and also single-engine stalls. Use caution to maintain plenty of altitude because the rate of descent in stalls is exceedingly high.

15. SPINS.

a. SPIN CHARACTERISTICS AND LIMITATIONS.

(1) There is no tendency for the airplane to spin inadvertently, either in the cruising or landing attitude. The airplane will recover from a spin up to the half-turn mark almost instantly when pressure is relaxed on either rudder or elevator

controls. After that the spin tends to tighten and acceleration increases. The airplane will lose approximately 2000 ft per turn.

(2) With the landing gear and flaps up, the airplane falls off slowly and deliberately. At the end of a 180° turn, the nose of the airplane will be nearly straight down. Rate of descent is high, although forward velocity does not increase appreciably during a half turn.

(3) With the landing gear and flaps down, spinning characteristics are similar to those of the airplane in the clean condition. In addition, continuous and fairly severe buffeting occurs and the spin is oscillatory in nature. Recovery is considerably slower than when the airplane is in the clean condition.

(4) Deliberate spins are prohibited.

CAUTION

Very high control forces, coupled with extremely high rate of descent, may be expected in a developed spin.

b. **RECOVER METHODS FOR SPINS.** — In case of an accidental spin, conventional recovery methods should be used. Recovery is easy during the first one and one-half turns and can be made without great difficulty after two and one-half turns by abrupt reversal of the rudder and the elevator. If there is no definite indication of regaining control in a developed spin below 5000 feet, abandon the airplane.

16. ACROBATICS.

The following maneuvers will be permitted in the normal load condition at a gross weight of not more than 28,220 lbs. At a load greater than this, no maneuvers or acrobatics of any type will be permitted. (See section II, paragraphs 1 and 2.)

a. Half Roll.

b. Normal Loop.

c. Immelman.

d. Chandelle.

e. Slow Rolls (speed not more than 350 mph ias.)

f. Vertical Reversement (speed not more than 250 mph ias).

17. DIVING.

a. **GENERAL.**

(1) Unless normal rated power is being used for tactical purposes, dives should be started with the rpm and manifold pressure set at some cruis-

ing value. This will cause the governor to act with less time lag as airspeed increases than if the take-off setting of the propeller governor were used. The throttles may be closed gradually, as the airplane increases speed, to assist in holding down engine rpm and to regulate manifold pressure.

(2) During dives, the mixture controls should be in the "AUTO RICH" position. The auxiliary blowers should be in "NEUTRAL" for all dives except those incident to military tactics at high altitudes.

(3) Once the airplane has been trimmed for an airspeed of 275 mph, no further trimming should be necessary.

b. **HIGH-SPEED DIVES AND STALLS.**—In high-speed dives and accelerated stalls compressibility effects in the form of buffeting and a tendency toward nose heaviness occur at a speed approximately 70 per cent of the speed of sound. The approximate variation of this speed with altitude is shown by the diving-speed limitations in paragraph 1 *b* (7). A pullup of at least 2.5 gs can still be made after this speed has been reached. Buffeting occurs at about 2 gs during pullups at speeds above approximately 60 per cent of the speed of sound, but the airplane can be pulled up through the buffeting region until an accelerated stall is produced.

(1) Do not enter a dive with the airplane trimmed nose heavy. Trim for approximately 275 mph ias, and push into the dive. It probably will not be necessary to use the trim tabs for recovery, although the stick forces will be fairly high at high speeds. In any case, use the trim tab slowly and cautiously.

(2) If buffeting occurs during the dive, begin a gradual pullup immediately. The buffeting may become more severe, but the airplane can be pulled up to about 2.5 gs at 30,000 feet, and to increased gs at lower altitudes, before it stalls.

(3) The accelerated stall is similar to the normal low-speed stall, excepting that buffeting may occur before the stall is reached and the pitching motion, in the stall, is considerably more violent.

(4) If external load items are carried, use caution in making high-speed dives and pullouts. See paragrape 1 *a* (6). In all cases, avoid violent movement of the controls if the airplane is buffeting.

c. DIVING LIMITATIONS

MAXIMUM DIVING
RPM   3060

See paragraph *1 a* (6). In all cases, avoid violent movement of the controls if the airplane is buffeting.

box mounted on the upper right side of the pilot's compartment. Desired color combinations can be selected and "keyed" by the button switch adjacent to the switches. *(See 3, figure 8.)*

b. A retractable landing light is installed in the lower surface of each outer wing panel. Two lights mounted on either side of the nose gear, are for use while taxiing. The control switches are on the pilot's electrical panel. *(See figure 24.)*

18. NIGHT FLYING.

a. The position lights are controlled by an "ON," "OFF," "DIM" toggle switch on the main electrical panel. *(See 14, figure 24.)* The recognition lights are controlled by an individual switch

Note

Limit the use of the recognition and landing lights as much as possible. Switch off the landing lights and use the taxiing lights as soon as possible after landing.

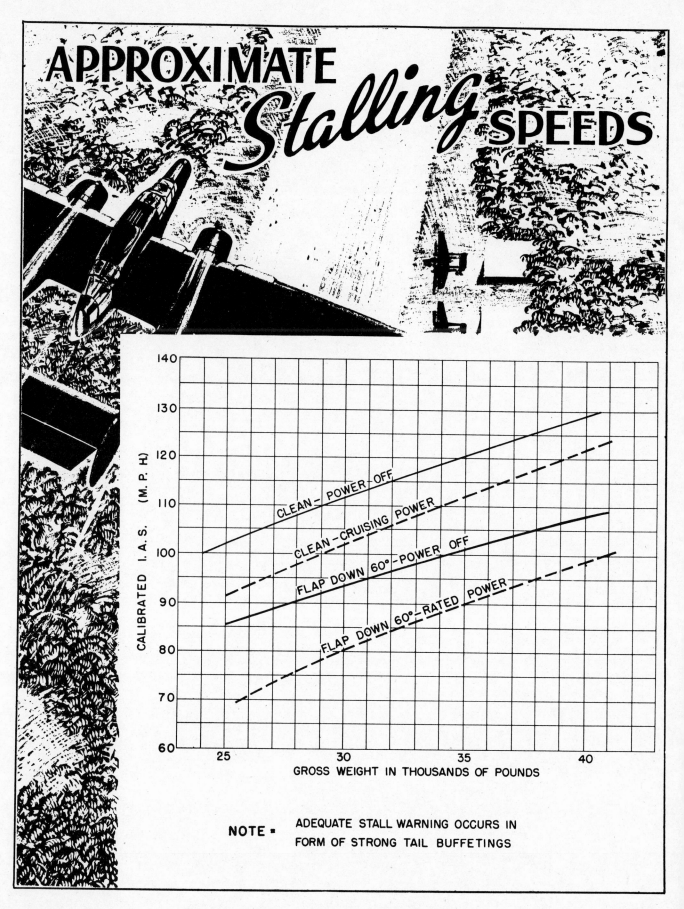

Figure 47A — Approximate Stalling Speeds

19. APPROACH AND LANDING.

a. ENGINE AND FLIGHT CONTROL SETTINGS.

(1) AUTOMATIC PILOT: Disengage.

(2) PROPELLER SWITCHES: "AUTOMATIC."

(3) PROPELLER CONTROLS: Set at 2300 rpm.

(4) FUEL SELECTOR: Fullest main tanks.

(5) MIXTURE: "AUTO-RICH."

(6) AUXILIARY BLOWER: "NEUTRAL."

(7) CROSS FEED: "OFF."

(8) FUEL BOOSTER PUMPS: "HIGH."

(9) COWL FLAPS: One-quarter open.

(10) DE-ICER: "OFF."

(11) ANTI-ICER: "OFF."

(12) COMPARTMENT HEATER: "OFF."

(13) TURRET GUNS: Stowed.

(14) LANDING GEAR: "DOWN." Check visually by reading indicator, and by retarding the throttle to check by the horn.

(15) HYDRAULIC & ACCUMULATOR PRESS: 800-1100 psi.

(16) CARBURETOR AIR CLEANER: "OFF."

(17) LANDING FLAPS: "DOWN."

b. FLIGHT TECHNIQUE.
The landing gear should be lowered during the down-wind leg of the approach. It is recommended that the flaps be lowered in two stages: at the half-way point of the base leg approach, lower the flaps one-half; in the final stage of approach, lower them all the way.

c. RECOMMENDED APPROACH SPEEDS.
Because the "approach" may be made in numerous ways and with varying distances, all involving a gradual cutting down in speed and power consistent with the type of approach used, the speeds given below are for use just prior to reaching the field ("over the fence" speeds).

(1) POWER ON: 105-110 MPH IAS.

(2) POWER OFF: 115 MPH IAS.

d. APPROACH AND LANDING WITH ONE ENGINE INOPERATIVE.

(1) Make approach with sufficient altitude and with slightly more speed than required for two-engine approach.

(2) "Wash out" (reduce) the rudder trim tab as the throttle is pulled back.

e. COLD WEATHER LANDING.

(1) CARBURETOR HEAT AND COWL FLAPS.

(a) Always land with carburetor heat "ON." Besides ice prevention, carburetor heat is necessary when landing to aid vaporization of fuel when it is found necessary to continue around without landing. The landing approach may cool the engine enough so that it will not pick up in an emergency due to poor fuel vaporization. Keep carburetor air temperature below 45°C (113°F) indicated to avoid loss of power due to excessive heat. (See figure 68.)

(b) Upon landing, the cowl flaps should be opened immediately. The airplane should be taxied to the line with carburetor heat "ON." Temperature inversions are common in winter in Arctic regions and the ground air may be 15° to 30°C (27° to 54°F) colder than at altitude. Therefore, care must be taken to avoid rapid cooling when letting down. If possible maintain cylinder head temperatures above 100°C (212°F).

(2) ELECTRICAL EQUIPMENT.—Electric suits should be turned off at least one-minute before the final approach and every effort should be made to reduce the use of electrical equipment to save the battery when rpm is lowered and the generators cut out.

f. CROSS WIND LANDING PROCEDURE.

(1) Make the approach longer than ordinary with power ON in order to establish a heading parallel to the runway.

(2) If the wind velocity is high, keep the up-wind wing slightly low to prevent drifting.

(3) Just before ground contact is made, reduce power, level the wings, and align the airplane with the runway.

(4) Lower the nose soon after contact is made to prevent yawing or hunting of the nose during the ground run immediately following contact. Do not let the nose wheel bounce once contact has been established.

(5) Apply brakes normally to control the deceleration and to maintain a straight heading.

(6) Cross wind landings on ice are particularly dangerous, due to the loss of maneuverability caused by lack of traction. Brakes should be used sparingly and not until absolutely necessary. Wheels should not be locked, especially on icy runways. Airplanes equipped with snow and ice tread tires offer better control under these conditions.

g. **TAKE-OFF IF LANDING IS NOT COMPLETED.**

(1) **THROTTLE:** Apply gradually.

(2) **ELEVATOR TRIM TAB:** Adjust for level flight.

(3) **FLAPS:** Retract one-half.

CAUTION

Retract flaps to one-half only when an airspeed of 125 mph and an altitude of at least 300 feet has been gained.

(4) **THROTTLE:** Maintain at 42 in. Hg until flaps are retracted.

(5) **FLAPS:** Full up.

CAUTION

Retract flaps fully and at the same time raise the nose when an airspeed of 140 mph and an altitude of at least 500 feet has been gained.

20. STOPPING ENGINES.

a. **PROCEDURE.**

(1) Shift auxiliary blowers before stopping engines in order to de-sludge the mechanism.

(2) If necessary, idle the engine until the cylinder head temperature is below 240°C.

(3) If a cold weather start is expected dilute the engine oil. See paragraph b, following.

(4) Leave the propeller controls in "INC. RPM."

(5) Stop each engine by moving the mixture controls to "IDLE CUT-OFF," and simultaneously opening the throttles fully.

(6) When the engines have stopped turn all switches "OFF."

b. **OPERATION OF OIL DILUTION SYSTEM.** If a cold weather start is anticipated, the oil should be diluted as follows:

(1) Operate engine to 1000-1200 RPM.

(2) Fuel booster pumps "OFF."

(3) Maintain oil temperatures above 5°C and below 50°C.

(4) On P-61A airplanes and P-61B airplanes prior to 42-39498 the dilution time periods for anticipated ground temperatures are as follows:

Anticipated Temperatures		Time
+ 4.4°C to —12.2°C	(+40°F to +10°F)	3 minutes
—12.2°C to —28.9°C	(+10°F to —20°F)	7 minutes
—28.9°C to —45.6°C	(—20°F to —50°F)	12 minutes

(5) On P-61B airplanes subsequent to 42-39498 periods are as follows:

Anticipated Temperatures		Time
+ 4.4°C to —12.2°C	(+40°F to +10°F)	3 minutes
—12.2°C to —28.9°C	(+10°F to —20°F)	6 minutes
—28.9°C to —45.6°C	(—20°F to —50°F)	9 minutes

CAUTION

If oil temperatures cannot be maintained below 50°C during dilution period, stop engines, release the oil dilution switches, and allow the oil to cool well below 40°C. When cooled sufficiently, restart engines, dilute remainder of time period, stop engines, and release the dilution switches. Repeat the procedure as necessary.

(6) Add one minute dilution for each additional 5°C (9°F) below —50°C (—58°F).

(7) Only in very extreme weather, where temperatures go below —12.2°C (10°F), will there be any necessity for diluting more than three minutes.

(8) In extremely cold weather, adequate dilution will prevent oil cooler or oil line failures due to high pressure developed by the oil scavenge pumps when the engine is started. However, for conservative operation, it is desirable to heat the oil lines, the oil cooler, and the accessories at the same time the portion of the engine forward of the diaphragm is being heated.

21. BEFORE LEAVING THE PILOT'S COMPARTMENT.

a. **ALL SWITCHES:** "Off" except generator switches.

b. **FUEL SELECTOR VALVES:** On.

c. **PARKING BRAKE:** Off after wheel chocks are in place.

d. **UPPER ENGINE COWL FLAPS:** "OPEN."

Note

In warm weather, leave all cowl flaps "OPEN."

e. **FLIGHT CONTROLS:** Locked. Move controls until the surfaces lock. Throttles must be "CLOSED."

f. Upon leaving the airplane, leave the windows open slightly to permit circulation of air, and close and lock the entrance doors.

1. AIRSPEED CORRECTION CHARTS.

a. The correction chart below applies only to those P-61A airplanes having the static pressure source built into the pitot tube on the vertical mast below the crew nacelle nose. *(See figure 48.)*

Calibrated Indicated Airspeed (MPH)	FLAPS UP		FLAPS DOWN	
	Pilot's I.A.S. (mph)	Altimeter Correction (ft)*	Pilot's I.A.S. (mph)	Altimeter Correction (ft)*
100			95	33
120	112	78	117	25
140	132	81	140	3
160	152	86		
180	172	90		
200	192	96		
220	212	104		
240	232	114		
260	253	126		
280	273	141		
300	293	157		
350	343	181		
400	393	213		

*Altimeter correction shown is applicable at sea level conditions only. For all other conditions, divide tabulated correction by air density ratio. ADD CORRECTION TO ALTIMETER READING TO OBTAIN PRESSURE ALTITUDE.

b. The correction chart below applies only to those P-61A airplanes having a flush static source built into the plastic crew nacelle nose section *(See figure 48.)*

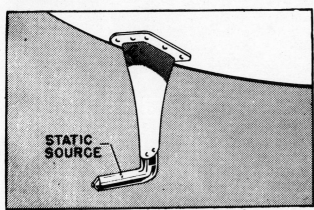

Calibrated Indicated Airspeed (MPH)	FLAPS UP		FLAPS DOWN	
	Pilot's I.A.S. (mph)	Altimeter Correction (ft)*	Pilot's I.A.S. (mph)	Altimeter Correction (ft)*
100	101	—5	100	0
120	122	—10	120	5
140	142	—15	139	10
160	163	—25	158	20
180	183	—40		
200	204	—60		
220	224	—85		
240	245	—110		
260	265	—140		
280	286	—170		
300	306	—210		
350	358	—315		
400	410	—440		

*Altimeter correction shown is applicable at sea level conditions only. For all other conditions, divide tabulated correction by air density ratio. ADD CORRECTION TO ALTIMETER READING TO OBTAIN PRESSURE ALTITUDE.

c. The airspeed correction for P-61B airplanes with the flaps up is the same as that given for P-61A airplanes with the flush static source (see paragraph *b*, preceding).

FLAPS DOWN	
Pilot's I.A.S. (mph)	Calibrated Indicated Airspeed (MPH)
100	105
120	125
140	145

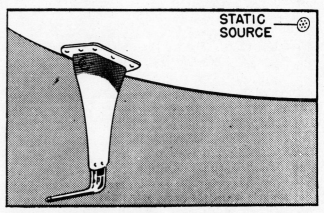

STATIC SOURCE

Figure 48—Pitot Static and Flush Static Installations

POWER PLANT CHART

AIRCRAFT MODEL(S)	PROPELLER(S)	ENGINE MODEL(S)
P-61A, P-61B	CURTISS ELECTRIC No. 714-7C2-12 FULL FEATHERING	R-2800-10, -65

GAUGE READING	FUEL PRESS.	OIL PRESS.	OIL TEMP.	COOLANT TEMP.	WATER PRESSURE (FLIGHT) #/SQ.IN		
DESIRED	17-19 without water 22-24 with water	75-80	60-95		22-24		

MAXIMUM PERMISSABLE DIVING RPM: 3060
MINIMUM RECOMMENDED CRUISE RPM: 1450
MAXIMUM RECOMMENDED TURBO RPM:

OIL GRADE: (S) 1120 (W) 1100
FUEL GRADE: 100/130, SPEC. AN-F-48

WAR EMERGENCY* (COMBAT EMERGENCY)			MILITARY POWER (NON-COMBAT EMERGENCY)			OPERATING CONDITION			NORMAL RATED (MAXIMUM CONTINUOUS)			MAXIMUM CRUISE (NORMAL OPERATION)		
5 MINUTES			15 MINUTES			TIME LIMIT MAX. CYL. HD. TEMP.			UNLIMITED			UNLIMITED		
260°C			260°C						232°C			232°C		
A.R.			A.R.			MIXTURE			A.R.			A.L.		
2700			2700			R.P.M.			2550			2230		
MANIF. PRESS.	SUPER-CHARGER	FUEL (2) Gal/Min	MANIF. PRESS.	SUPER-CHARGER	FUEL (2) Gal/Min	STD. TEMP. °C	PRESSURE ALTITUDE	STD. TEMP. °F	MANIF. PRESS.	SUPER-CHARGER	FUEL GPH (3)	MANIF. PRESS.	SUPER-CHARGER	FUEL GPH (3)
						-55.0	40,000 FT.	-67.0						
						-55.0	38,000 FT.	-67.0						
						-55.0	36,000 FT.	-67.0						
						-52.4	34,000 FT.	-62.3						
						-48.4	32,000 FT.	-55.1						
						-44.4	30,000 FT.	-48.0				F.T.	HIGH	87
			F.T.	HIGH	3	-40.5	28,000 FT.	-40.9	F.T.	HIGH	180	36.0	HIGH	97
			F.T.	HIGH	4	-36.5	26,000 FT.	-33.7	F.T.	HIGH	200	36.0	HIGH	97
						-32.5	24,000 FT.	-26.5	F.T.	HIGH	220	F.T.	LOW	91
F.T.	HIGH	4	F.T.	HIGH	4	-28.6	22,000 FT.	-19.4	49.5	HIGH	230	35.5	LOW	96
F.T.	HIGH	4	53.0	HIGH	5	-24.6	20,000 FT.	-12.3	49.5	HIGH	225	35.5	LOW	93
F.T.	HIGH	4	F.T.	LOW	4	-20.7	18,000 FT.	-5.2	F.T.	LOW	235	35.5	LOW	91
60.0	HIGH	5	54.0	LOW	5	-16.7	16,000 FT.	2.0	49.5	LOW	245	35.5	LOW	89
F.T.	LOW	4	54.0	LOW	5	-12.7	14,000 FT.	9.1	49.5	LOW	240	F.T.	NEUT	84
60.0	LOW	5	54.0	LOW	5	-8.8	12,000 FT.	16.2	49.5	LOW	235	34.0	NEUT	90
60.0	LOW	5	54.0	LOW	4	-4.8	10,000 FT.	23.4	49.5	LOW	230	34.0	NEUT	88
60.0	LOW	5	54.0	LOW	4	-0.8	8,000 FT.	30.5	44.5	NEUT	205	34.0	NEUT	86
60.0	LOW	5	F.T.	NEUT	4	3.1	6,000 FT.	37.6	44.5	NEUT	200	34.0	NEUT	84
F.T.	NEUT	4	53.0	NEUT	5	7.1	4,000 FT.	44.7	44.5	NEUT	195	34.0	NEUT	81
F.T.	NEUT	4	53.0	NEUT	4	11.0	2,000 FT.	51.8	44.5	NEUT	190	34.0	NEUT	79
60.0	NEUT	4	53.0	NEUT	4	15.0	SEA LEVEL	59.0	44.5	NEUT	185	34.0	NEUT	77

GENERAL NOTES

(2) Gal/Min: APPROXIMATE U.S. GALLON PER MINUTE PER ENGINE
(3) GPH: APPROXIMATE U.S. GALLON PER HOUR PER ENGINE.
F.T.: MEANS FULL THROTTLE OPERATION.
VALUES ARE FOR LEVEL FLIGHT WITH RAM.

FOR COMPLETE CRUISING DATA SEE APPENDIX II
NOTE: TO DETERMINE CONSUMPTION IN BRITISH IMPERIAL UNITS, MULTIPLY BY 10 THEN DIVIDE BY 12. RED FIGURES ARE PRELIMINARY SUBJECT TO REVISION AFTER FLIGHT CHECK.

TAKE-OFF CONDITIONS:
2700 R.P.M. AND 54.0 IN. HG.

CONDITIONS TO AVOID:
DO NOT CRUISE AT 1700 OR 2000 RPM BECAUSE OF EXCESSIVE VIBRATION.

SPECIAL NOTES

* WAR EMERGENCY POWER AVAILABLE ONLY WITH WATER INJECTION.

BECAUSE OF DANGEROUS PROPELLER VIBRATION, OPERATION WITH ENGINE RPM SETTINGS OF 1800 TO 2300 IS RESTRICTED TO THE TIME REQUIRED TO PASS THROUGH THIS RANGE WHEN CHANGING POWER SETTINGS.

AAFMC-526
8-1-44

DATA AS OF 10-1-46 BASED ON FLIGHT TEST

POSSIBLE ICING −10° TO +15°
DESIRED +15 TO +32°

MAXIMUM WITHOUT
WATER INJECTION +32°

MAXIMUM WITH
WATER INJECTION +54°

MINIMUM FOR TAKE-OFF 40
DESIRED 60 TO 85
MAXIMUM 100

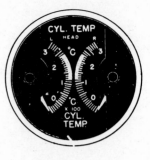

DESIRED 120 TO 232
MAXIMUM 260

MINIMUM 60
DESIRED 65 TO 95
MAXIMUM 100

MAXIMUM FLAPS DOWN 175
MAXIMUM 430

FOR F-61A AIRPLANES ONLY

MAXIMUM WITHOUT
WATER INJECTION 54
AUTO-LEAN 25 TO 36
AUTO-RICH 36 TO 49
MAXIMUM WITH
WATER INJECTION 60

WITHOUT WATER INJECTION
    MINIMUM 17
       DESIRED 17 TO 19
    MAXIMUM 21

WITH WATER INJECTION
    MINIMUM 22
       DESIRED 22 TO 24
    MAXIMUM 26

MAXIMUM WITH FLAPS OR GEAR DOWN 175
MAXIMUM IAS 430
THE INSTRUMENT SETTING IS SUCH THAT
THE RED POINTER WILL MOVE TO INDICATE
THE LIMITING STRUCTURAL AIRSPEED OF 430
MPH OR THE AIRSPEED REPRESENTING THE
LIMITING MACH NO. OF .70, WHICHEVER IS LESS.
(FOR F-61B AIRPLANES ONLY)

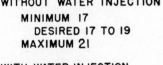

MINIMUM 22
   DESIRED 22 TO 24
MAXIMUM 24

CRUISING 1450 TO 1800
DANGEROUS PROPELLER
VIBRATION 1800 TO
2300
MAXIMUM CONTINUOUS
2300 TO 2550
MAXIMUM R.P.M. 2700

Figure 48A—Instrument Range Markings

Section IV
EMERGENCY OPERATING
INSTRUCTIONS

1. ENGINE FAILURE DURING FLIGHT.

a. With one engine off and propeller windmilling, the live engine pulling military power and rudder trim neutral, the airplane can be controlled down to its normal stalling speed (gear and flaps up) of 100 mph ias. The ability of the pilot to "catch" the airplane and maintain directional and lateral control under conditions of military power and slow forward speeds, coupled with sudden engine failure, will depend upon the speed and accuracy with which the pilot can apply the necessary corrective control deflections. Under normal conditions of flight, it will not be necessary to reduce the power of the live engine. Therefore on inoperative engine:

(1) THROTTLE: "CLOSE."

(2) FEATHERING SWITCH: Feather.

(3) MIXTURE CONTROL: "IDLE CUT-OFF."

(4) FUEL SELECTOR VALVE: "OFF."

(5) COWL FLAPS: "CLOSED."

(6) IGNITION SWITCH: "OFF."

(7) LIVE ENGINE MIXTURE CONTROL: "AUTO RICH."

CAUTION

Avoid violent maneuvers. Maintain sufficient airspeed when making turns with inoperative engine down.

Note

Single-engine service ceiling (normal rated power on live engine) at normal gross weight (27,000 pounds) is approximately 16,000 feet.

b. If, for any reason, forward speed falls below the minimum for control, regain speed by losing altitude and not by applying additional power.

c. TRIMMING AIRPLANE FOR STABLE FLIGHT WITH ONE ENGINE INOPERATIVE. No unusual characteristics. There is no necessity to trim for lateral or longitudinal stability. Rudder trim will provide directional stability.

d. LANDING WITH ONE ENGINE INOPERATIVE.—Single-engine approach and landing technique is largely a matter of training, experience, and the desire of the individual pilot. However, the following is recommended:

(1) Make a fairly high approach with partial flap deflection, 30° (one-half) recommended.

(2) Maintain a safe speed and altitude until it is certain that there is no danger of under-shooting.

(3) Deflect flaps 40° (two-thirds). When landing is assured, deflect flaps to full 60°.

(4) The decision to go around again because of possible over-shooting should be made at a time when the airplane still has a safe margin of altitude.

(5) If it is necessary to go around again, raise the landing gear **immediately** to reduce drag. Apply power gradually, raise flaps SLOWLY to 20° (one-third) as soon as speed permits.

2. WAR EMERGENCY POWER (WATER INJECTION).

To obtain war emergency power:

a. THROTTLE: Full "OPEN."

b. POWER SWITCH: On.

Note

When the water injection is turned on a lapse of a few seconds will occur before it takes hold. The effect is gradual rather than immediate.

3. FIRE.

a. FIRE EXTINGUISHERS.—A two-pound capacity carbon dioxide hand fire extinguisher, Type 4TB, is clipped to the bulkhead at the aft end of the gunner's compartment near the left-hand cockpit rail. *(See figure 63.)* A one-quart carbon tetrachloride hand fire extinguisher, Type A2, is located in each main landing gear wheel well. On P-61B airplanes they are reached through access doors marked "FIRE EXTINGUISHER" in the outboard side of the main gear wheel wells. Late P-61B airplanes carry a carbon dioxide, hand fire extinguisher in the radio operator's compartment.

b. USE OF EQUIPMENT.

(1) To operate the crew nacelle CO_2 extinguisher, grasp the extinguisher with one hand and swing the horn upward and discharge the gas as close as possible to the base of the fire. Control the discharge with the trigger.

(2) To operate the Type A-2 extinguishers stowed in the wheel well, turn the handle and operate as a pump. Avoid exposure to smoke and fumes. Avoid personal exposure to smoke and fumes.

c. FIRES IN FLIGHT.

(1) Notify crew members to attach their parachutes and await further instructions.

(2) ENGINE FIRES.

(a) FEATHERING SWITCH: Feather.
(b) MIXTURE CONTROL: "IDLE CUT-OFF."
(c) FUEL SELECTOR VALVE: "OFF."

Note

FUEL SELECTOR VALVE: "ON" for the unaffected engine.

(d) CROSS FEED VALVE: "OFF."
(e) COWL FLAPS: ¼ open.
(f) IGNITION: "OFF."
(g) Do not restart engine.

If fire cannot be controlled through the above procedure and conditions permit, land immediately; otherwise abandon the aircraft.

(3) WING FIRES.
(a) Turn all light switches for wing on fire "OFF."

Position Light
Recognition Lights (right wing only)
Landing Light

(b) If time permits, gain altitude.
(c) Attempt to extinguish the fire by side slipping the airplane away from the fire where possible.
(d) If the fire continues open the emergency exists. If a landing cannot be made safely,

head the airplane toward an unpopulated area, set the controls, and bail out.

(4) CREW NACELLE FIRES.
(a) Close all windows and ventilators.
(b) If electrical fire, turn master switch "OFF." If leaking fuel or hydraulic line, shut off valves.
(c) Put fire extinguisher into use IMMEDIATELY. It is adequate for fighting fires only in the earliest stages.

(5) GROUND FIRES.—If an engine fire starts from back firing when starting the engine:
(a) Continue running the engine to suck the fire through the engine.
(b) Keep turning the engine over with the starter (if necessary).
(c) If the fire continues, shut off the fuel supply to the engine. Use the hand fire extinguishers while the engine is running.

4. ALARM BELL.

When the pilot makes the decision to abandon, crash land or ditch the airplane, the crew should be warned as soon as possible.

a. The following alarm bell procedure will be followed:

(1) TO ABANDON AIRCRAFT.
(a) Warning—spoken warning on the interphone.
(b) Warning—three short rings on the alarm bell.
(c) Bail out—bail out order on the interphone.
(d) Bail out—one long ring on the alarm bell.

(2) DITCHING OR CRASH LANDING.
(a) Warning—spoken warning on the interphone.
(b) Warning—six short rings on the alarm bell.
(c) Prepare for ditching or crash landing (brace just before impact)—one long sustained ring on the alarm bell.

b. The warning bell operating switch is located beside the left cockpit rail between the gunner's and pilot's positions. It is accessible to both gunner and pilot.

c. There are two warning bells: one beneath the radio operator's table on the right side of the crew nacelle, the other on the left side of the crew nacelle near the gunner's seat.

5. EMERGENCY EXITS. *(See figure 49.)*

a. PILOT'S AND GUNNER'S EMERGENCY EXIT.—The right-hand portion of the enclosure, aft of the gunner's windshield, is released to fly away by turning the emergency release handle and pushing sharply. The pilot and gunner crawl through the opening onto the inner wing.

(1) The gunner's seat is opposite the emergency exit.

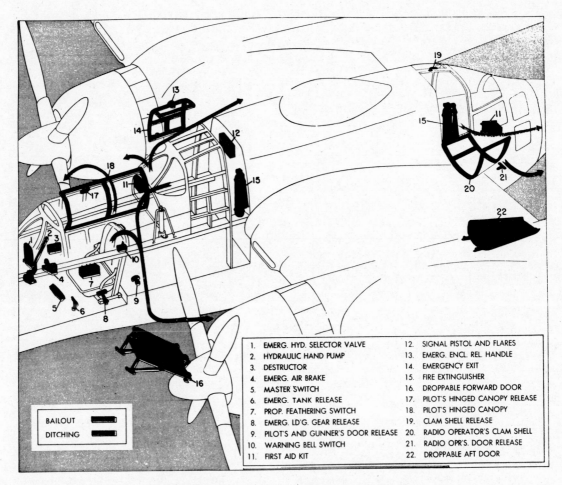

1. EMERG. HYD. SELECTOR VALVE	12. SIGNAL PISTOL AND FLARES
2. HYDRAULIC HAND PUMP	13. EMERG. ENCL. REL. HANDLE
3. DESTRUCTOR	14. EMERGENCY EXIT
4. EMERG. AIR BRAKE	15. FIRE EXTINGUISHER
5. MASTER SWITCH	16. DROPPABLE FORWARD DOOR
6. EMERG. TANK RELEASE	17. PILOT'S HINGED CANOPY RELEASE
7. PROP. FEATHERING SWITCH	18. PILOT'S HINGED CANOPY
8. EMERG. LD'G. GEAR RELEASE	19. CLAM SHELL RELEASE
9. PILOT'S AND GUNNER'S DOOR RELEASE	20. RADIO OPERATOR'S CLAM SHELL
10. WARNING BELL SWITCH	21. RADIO OPR'S. DOOR RELEASE
11. FIRST AID KIT	22. DROPPABLE AFT DOOR

BAILOUT ▬▬

DITCHING ▬▬

Figure 49 — Emergency Equipment and Exits

b. RADIO OPERATOR'S EMERGENCY EXIT.
The radio operator's entrance door is released by pulling sharply on the red emergency release handle located on the lower left side of the compartment and AT THE SAME TIME pulling on the normal release. This removes the hinge pins, allowing the door to drop free to be carried away by the airstream.

c. FORWARD EMERGENCY EXIT DOOR.—
On late P-61A airplanes and P-61B airplanes the front entrance door also serves as an emergency exit. To use it as an emergency exit the nose gear must be in the down position. To release, turn the door handle clockwise, then pull the emergency release handle, located on the left hand cockpit rail, between the pilot and gunner, allowing the door to fall free.

6. EMERGENCY LANDING GEAR OPERATION.

a. EMERGENCY EXTENSION.—In the event of failure of the main hydraulic system, move the landing gear selector valve knob *(see 2, figure 16)* to the "DOWN" position and, with hand pump selector valve *(see 12, figure 8)* on "SYSTEM," operate the hand pump until the landing gear is locked DOWN. If this method fails, leave the selector valve knob "DOWN" and pull the landing gear emergency release handle *(see 9, figure 7)* to extend the landing gear. Hold the handle up until the nose gear is locked down, then release.

Note

When using the emergency release, reduce speed to 130 mph ias or less. If the main gear fails to release, shake the airplane longitudinally.

b. EMERGENCY RETRACTION.—Late P-61B airplanes are equipped with an emergency retraction mechanism for the landing gear. To operate, pull the emergency landing gear handle up and place is in the holder about four inches above the floor of the cockpit. With the down lock held open the gear will retract on contact with the ground. Because of its position the nose gear will remain extended and the airplane will land on the nose wheel and booms.

7. EMERGENCY LANDING WITH WHEELS RETRACTED.

a. If time and other conditions permit, fire all 20-mm cannon ammunition toward an unpopulated area. Warn the crew of the crash landing as soon as possible by a spoken warning on the interphone and by sounding six short rings on the alarm bell.

b. Turn off the master heater switches, located on the generator control panel, at least two minutes before landing so that the fuel in the lines and combustion chambers may be consumed.

c. Completely drain the airplane's oxygen supply by turning the red "EMERGENCY" knob on each oxygen regulator "ON."

d. Fully extend wing flaps.

e. Make approach just above stalling speed.

f. Turn master switch and battery switches "OFF" before the airplane touches the ground.

g. Land at slowest practical speed. Just prior to impact give a warning to brace by sounding one long sustained ring on the alarm bell.

h. Precautions against fire must be taken immediately after landing.

i. First aid kits are stowed in both the forward and aft compartments.

8. EMERGENCY LANDING IN WATER.

a. PREPARATIONS FOR DITCHING.

(1) Preparations for ditching must not be left until the final moment. Warn the crew of the decision to ditch as soon as possible by interphone and by sounding six short rings on the alarm bell. The nature of the operation is such that adequate time must be allowed to conclude proper arrangements in advance. If the correct steps are taken the safety of the crew and the ultimate chances for rescue will be greatly enhanced.

(2) If the pilot reasonably believes that it will be necessary to ditch the airplane, the SOS signal, time, and position should be given. This distress call should be made well in advance of actual ditching. If conditions make it unnecessary to carry out the operation, the call can always be cancelled.

(3) If time permits, all ammunition in the airplane should be fired. This is a safety measure that also serves to lighten the airplane and to attract nearby aircraft or ships. If external tanks or bombs are installed, they must be dropped before ditching the airplane.

(4) Both fore and aft entrance doors and the landing gear doors should be checked to be certain that they are securely closed and fastened. The radio operator's cam shell and the forward canopy should be opened just before the airplane is set on the water. This does away with the possibility of jamming upon impact. It is imperative that the crew leave the airplane without delay.

(5) All bright internal lights should be turned off in order to accustom the eyes to darkness. After ditching, all lights should be turned on in order to assist search in the event the airplane floats.

(6) It is absolutely essential that the airplane be ditched while there is sufficient fuel to permit a power-on landing. Final decision to ditch the airplane should be made when at least enough fuel for fifteen minutes' operation remains, unless the pilot is certain that he can reach land. Use of power assures adequate control and ability to flatten out the airplane for proper alighting on water.

b. LANDING.

(1) Landing gear must NOT be extended. Flaps may be lowered as much as 20° in order to reduce landing speed. Just prior to impact give a warning to brace by sounding one long sustained ring on the alarm bell.

(2) The airplane should alight with the tail down. There will be a slight primary impact as the rear of the airplane strikes, followed by a severe impact and a rapid stop. The higher the rate of speed at which the airplane is landed, the more severe the impact, the greater the danger of structural collapse. If the landing is made too fast, the airplane will tend to bounce, greatly increasing the danger of collapse.

(3) In a crosswind approach along a swell, the airplane should be ditched on the up-slope of the swell.

(4) In a steep swell, the pilot should ditch along the top of the swell unless there is a very strong crosswind. In ditching across the swell the airplane should be put down on an up-slope toward the top.

c. Shortly before the airplane touches the water, each crew member should unfasten his parachute and free himself from the straps. BE CERTAIN THAT BOTH THE SAFETY BELT AND SHOULDER HARNESS ARE IN PLACE AND FASTENED.

WARNING

In airplanes equipped with sighting stations, stow the sighting arm and swing it around so that it is not in front of the crew member.

d. ABANDONING THE AIRPLANE.

(1) The crew should be prepared to abandon the airplane as soon as it comes to rest. The radio

Figure 50 — Abandoning the Airplane in the Water

operator will leave through his clam shell opening, the gunner through the forward emergency exit, and the pilot through the pilot's hinged canopy. (See figure 50.)

9. PROPELLER FEATHERING.

    a. FEATHERING IN FLIGHT.—In case of engine failure in flight, when it is desirable to stop rotation of the engine, or when practice feathering, use the following procedure:

    (1) THROTTLE: "CLOSED."

    (2) FEATHERING SWITCH: "FEATHER."

    (3) MIXTURE CONTROL: "IDLE CUT-OFF."

    (4) FUEL SUPPLY: "OFF" to idle engine.

    (5) IGNITION SWITCH: "OFF" after propeller stops rotating.

CAUTION

Practice feathering in flight should not be attempted unless the pilot is thoroughly familiar with the correct procedure for stopping and starting the engines in flight, as well as with the flight characteristics of the airplane operating with one idle engine.

    (6) If the propeller fails to respond to the feather procedure, then feather by holding the selector switch in the "DEC RPM" position.

    (7) If the propeller still fails to feather, attempt to windmill it at the lowest possible rpm. The propeller will windmill at a speed proportionate to the airspeed, making it desirable to fly not more than 20 to 30 mph above the stalling speed. Place the engine controls as in paragraphs *a*(1), (3), (4), and (5), preceding.

    (8) If severe vibration exists, the tendency to vibrate can be reduced by flying at the absolute minimum air speed. Frequently the engine will seize and stop the windmilling. At other times when the engine seizes the reduction gear housing will fail, allowing the propeller, the propeller shaft, and reduction gearing to be carried away. In other cases of engine seizure, only the reduction gearing will be wrecked which relieves the windmilling propeller of the engine drag and permits it to windmill faster.

    c. UNFEATHERING.

    (1) THROTTLE: "CLOSED."

    (2) IGNITION: "ON."

    (3) PROPELLER CONTROL: "DEC RPM."

    (4) FUEL SUPPLY: "ON."

    (5) MIXTURE CONTROL: "AUTO-RICH."

    (6) Set feathering switch in the normal position and hold the selector switch in "INC RPM" until the engine speed reaches 800 rpm, then release the selector switch.

(7) If the engine has been allowed to cool, it must be thoroughly warmed up at about 800 rpm before being brought up to speed.

(8) When engine operating temperatures have been reached, place the selector switches in "AUTOMATIC," adjust throttle, propeller control and mixture levers to the desired power and engine rpm.

10. FUEL SYSTEM FAILURE DURING FLIGHT.
(See figures 28 and 31.)

a. FUEL PUMP FAILURE.—The fuel booster pump should maintain a fuel pressure sufficient for normal engine operation.

b. BOOSTER PUMP FAILURE.—If the engine fails, turn the selector valve to another tank and restart the engine.

c. FAILURE OF BOTH FUEL AND BOOSTER PUMPS ON ONE ENGINE.

(1) Turn "ON" the cross feed valve.

(2) Turn the booster pump on the operating engine to "HIGH."

(3) Restart the engine.

d. TANK ALLOWED TO RUN DRY.

(1) Turn the selector valve to a full tank.

(2) If both tanks on one side are dry, turn on the cross feed valve.

(3) Restart the engine.

Note

On airplanes having only outer wing bomb rack installations the auxiliary tank switches must be turned "OFF" when the tanks are empty. Otherwise, pressurized air will continue to flow from the auxiliary tanks thus keeping fuel from the wing tanks from reaching the engine.

e. BROKEN FUEL LINE.

(1) Turn the mixture control to "IDLE CUT-OFF" and the booster pump "OFF" on the side where the break occurs.

(2) Turn the selector valve to "OFF."

Note

If the cross feed valve is on, turn it "OFF."

(3) Feather the propeller on the affected engine.

(4) When the propeller stops rotating, cut the ignition switch on the inoperative engine.

(5) Operate the airplane on one engine. Watch for evidence of fire.

11. OIL SYSTEM FAILURE DURING FLIGHT.
(See figures 33 and 34.)

a. Turn mixture control to "IDLE CUT-OFF."

b. Turn the fuel selector valve "OFF" until the fuel is needed for the other engine.

c. Turn the booster pump "OFF."

d. Feather the propeller on the affected engine. When the propeller stops rotating, turn the ignition switch "OFF."

12. HYDRAULIC SYSTEM FAILURE.
(See figures 38 through 41.)

a. Hydraulic system failure may be caused by a leak in one of the lines or units, or failure of the engine-driven hydraulic pumps. Usually the failure will be indicated by low pressure gage reading (normal 850-1000 psi).

b. In case of a failure of the hydraulic system, all hydraulic equipment except the automatic pilot may be operated by the hand pump for a short time unless the fluid leaks out faster than the hand pump can supply pressure.

Note

Normally it will be advisable to save the hand pump pressure for flap and brake operation during landing. (On P-61B airplanes the flaps operate from the main pressure system.)

(1) If a leak occurs in the main system, the fluid in the accumulator and about one-third of the fluid in the main reservoir will be available for emergency operation.

(2) The hand pump (13) and the hand pump selector valve (12) are located to the right of the control column. *(See figure 8.)*

(3) TO OPERATE THE HAND PUMP.

(a) Turn the hand pump selector valve to either "SYSTEM" or "ACCUMULATOR" as required.

Note

Both the wing flap system and brake system operate from the accumulator on the P-61A airplane.

(b) Pump vigorously to produce the required pressure.

(c) Fluid is forced from the pump to a selector valve from which it may be directed to the unit to be operated.

(d) When the hand pump is not in use, the selector valve should be turned to "NEUTRAL."

13. BRAKE FAILURE.

a. Brakes are normally operated by fluid from the accumulator hydraulic system and regulated by the pilot's foot pedals.

b. In event of failure to the hydraulic pressure system, the brakes may be operated in the normal manner if sufficient pressure can be built up by use of the hand pump.

Note

It is highly possible that hydraulic pressure built up through the use of the hand pump will be expended in operating the wing flaps during an emergency.

c. For such a condition an emergency air brake system is provided. The release lever is located on the cockpit rail toward the left front corner. *(See figure 6-6)* Operation of the emergency air brake lever introduces air under pressure from a storage bottle into the brake lines. This forces the brakes on. The storage bottle contains sufficient air for approximately four applications of the brakes. Extreme caution should be used on snow and ice covered runways in order to avoid locking the brakes. Locked brakes will cause an uncontrollable skid which may result in serious damage to the airplane.

Note

After using the emergency air brake, upon return to a base, the lines should be bled and the storage bottle refilled to 425 psi.

14. MISCELLANEOUS EMERGENCY EQUIPMENT.

a. **FIRST AND KITS.**—Two first aid kits are furnished. One is attached to the gunner's armor plate. The second is located to the left and aft of the radio operator's access door.

b. **PYROTECHNIC EQUIPMENT.**—A type M-8 Very Pistol, signal cartridges, and parachute flares are carried in the gunner's compartment in a container fixed to the bulkhead aft of the gunner's seat. *(See 5, figure 63.)*

CAUTION

The pistol is cocked when the breech is closed. Do not stow the pistol loaded.

Section V
OPERATIONAL
EQUIPMENT

1. HEATING AND VENTILATING SYSTEM.

a. P-61A AIRPLANES. (See figure 51.)

(1) DESCRIPTION.—The air conditioning system for the P-61A airplanes consists of four fuel-air mixture heaters, a manifold to direct heat to the 20-mm cannon and the turret section, and three ventilators.

(2) VENTILATING SYSTEM.—A manually operated louvre type ventilator is built into the right side of each crew nacelle compartment and opens directly into the airstream. The radio operator's ventilator is located forward of his enclosure. (See 15, figure 56.) The pilot's (see 15, figure 8) and gunner's (see 11, figure 62) ventilators are located below their respective controls.

(3) HEATING SYSTEM.—The pilot's heater is located at the extreme forward end of his compartment. The gunner's heater is attached to the bulkhead to the right and aft of the gunner. The radio operator's heater is located beneath the cockpit floor in the left forward side of the compartment. The gun heater is located in the cannon bay at the aft end of the manifold. The left-hand engine supplies the fuel-air mixture for the gun and radio operator's heaters and the right-hand engine supplies the fuel-air mixture for the pilot's and gunner's heaters. Fuel for the heaters flows from the engine supercharger case through a solenoid operated valve to a header which directs the flows to two heaters. Burned gases are exhausted overboard through a line from each heater.

(a) The pilot's and gunner's heaters are operated from a single switch located on the generator control panel. (See 15, figure 44.) The gun and radio operator's heaters are operated from a switch on the radio operator's junction box. Pressure switches automatically turn off the heaters when there is insufficient fuel-air pressure to operate them.

b. P-61B AIRPLANES. (See figure 52.)

(1) DESCRIPTION. — The P-61B airplanes are equipped with two fuel-air type surface combustion heaters. The forward heater is mounted on the right-hand side of the bulkhead in the gunner's compartment and receives fuel from the right-hand engine. This heater provides heat for the forward compartment. The aft heater is mounted below the radio operator's floor and receives fuel from the left-hand engine. This heater provides heat for the radio operator and the guns. Ventilation also is provided through the heating system. On late P-61B airplanes a hinged plexiglass ventilating window is incorporated in the radio operator's enclosure.

(2) CONTROLS.

(a) FORWARD HEATER.—The forward heater control switches, marked "FWD CABIN," are located on the generator control panel. They consist of a master control switch with "ON" and "OFF" positions and an energizing switch with an "OFF" position and an on position labeled "TO START HOLD ON 10 SEC." A manual fuel pressure control, marked "CABIN HEAT," is installed on the right cockpit rail, immediately above the generator control panel.

(b) AFT HEATER.—The aft heater master control switch, labeled "CANNON," is located on the generator control panel. The aft heater energizing switch, marked "TO START HOLD ON 10 SEC.," and the circuit breaker switch, marked "HEATER," are both located on the right crew nacelle rail opposite the radio operator's seat. A manual, T-handle type, fuel pressure control, labeled "PULL UP TO INCREASE TEMPERATURE," is mounted on the right crew nacelle rail adjacent to the switches. (See figure 53.)

(c) AUTOMATIC SAFETY SWITCHES.— Three thermal safety switches, located on the output side of each heater, thermostatically shut off the glow coil when it reaches 49°C (250°F), the fuel-flow control shut-off valve when the heater output temperature reaches 121°C (250°F), and both the engine nacelle fuel-solenoid valve and the fuel-flow control shut-off valve when the temperature reaches 177°C (350°F).

(d) ANEMOSTAT CONTROLS.—An anemostat is installed at each of the three crew sta-

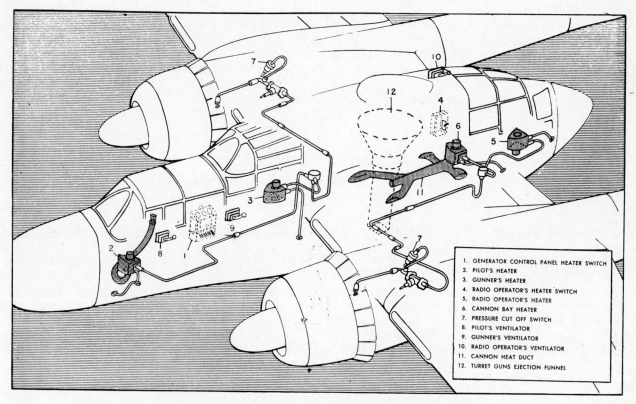

1. GENERATOR CONTROL PANEL HEATER SWITCH
2. PILOT'S HEATER
3. GUNNER'S HEATER
4. RADIO OPERATOR'S HEATER SWITCH
5. RADIO OPERATOR'S HEATER
6. CANNON BAY HEATER
7. PRESSURE CUT OFF SWITCH
8. PILOT'S VENTILATOR
9. GUNNER'S VENTILATOR
10. RADIO OPERATOR'S VENTILATOR
11. CANNON HEAT DUCT
12. TURRET GUNS EJECTION FUNNEL

Figure 51 — Heating and Ventilating System (P-61A)

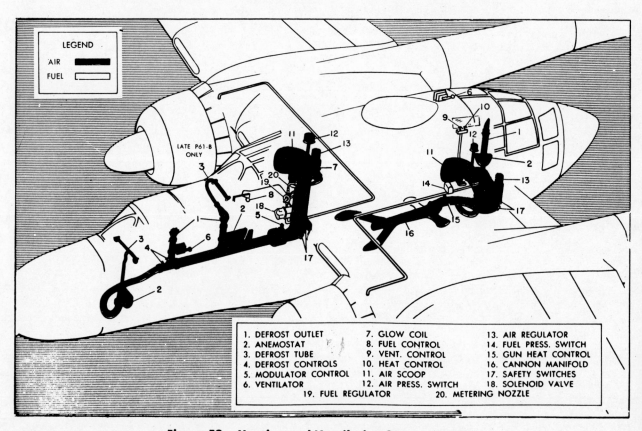

LEGEND

AIR

FUEL

LATE P61-B ONLY

1. DEFROST OUTLET	7. GLOW COIL	13. AIR REGULATOR
2. ANEMOSTAT	8. FUEL CONTROL	14. FUEL PRESS. SWITCH
3. DEFROST TUBE	9. VENT. CONTROL	15. GUN HEAT CONTROL
4. DEFROST CONTROLS	10. HEAT CONTROL	16. CANNON MANIFOLD
5. MODULATOR CONTROL	11. AIR SCOOP	17. SAFETY SWITCHES
6. VENTILATOR	12. AIR PRESS. SWITCH	18. SOLENOID VALVE
	19. FUEL REGULATOR	20. METERING NOZZLE

Figure 52 — Heating and Ventilating System (P-61B)

tions. Each anemostat is equipped with a "CABIN AIR" control having "OPEN" and "CLOSED" positions.

(e) **MODULATOR VALVE OVERRIDE CONTROLS.**—The override control for the forward heater is located on the floor at the left of the gunner's seat. The override control for the aft heater is a T-handle, labeled "PULL UP FOR VENTILATION WHEN HEATER IS OFF," installed on the right rail. *(See figure 53.)*

(3) OPERATION.

(a) **FORWARD HEATER.**

1. **TO START.**—Place the "FWD. CABIN" master control switch in the "ON" position. Hold the energizing switch up against the spring tension to energize the fuel-solenoid shut-off valve. This should be accomplished in 2 to 10 seconds. If heat is not noticeable within 45 seconds after the switch is released, repeat the procedure.

2. **TO INCREASE HEAT.**—Move the manual control lever, labeled "CABIN HEAT," from the "ON" to the "WARMER" position.

3. **TO STOP.**—Move the master control switch to the "OFF" position.

4. **TO SECURE VENTILATING AIR.** Open the modulator valve by opening the override control lever at the gunner's position. Place the anemostat "CABIN AIR" control in the "OPEN" position.

(b) **AFT HEATER.**

1. **TO START.**—Place the master control switch, marked "CANNON," in the "ON" position. Hold the aft heater energizing switch up against the spring tension for the 2 to 10 seconds necessary to energize the fuel-solenoid shut-off valve.

2. **TO INCREASE HEAT.**—Pull up the T-handle marked "PULL UP TO INCREASE TEMPERATURE." Turn the handle to lock it in position.

3. **TO STOP.**—To turn off the aft heater, place either the "CANNON" heater switch on the generator control panel or the "HEATER" circuit breaker in the radio operator's compartment in the "OFF" position.

4. **TO SECURE VENTILATING AIR.** Pull up the T-handle labeled "PULL UP FOR VENTILATION WHEN HEATER IS OFF." Turn the handle to lock it in position. This opens the modulator valve and permits air to enter the system. Place the "CABIN AIR" lever on the radio operator's anemostat in the "OPEN" position.

2. OXYGEN SYSTEM. *(See figure 54.)*

a. **DESCRIPTION.**—The airplane is equipped with a low pressure oxygen system operating at a working pressure of 425 psi.

b. **OXYGEN CYLINDERS.**—Oxygen is carried in twelve low pressure oxygen cylinders, six in each engine nacelle aft of the wheel well at the tail boom attaching angle. The two upper cylinders in each engine nacelle provide oxygen to the pilot, the two middle cylinders to the radio operator, and the two bottom cylinders to the gunner.

c. **REGULATORS.**—Three demand type regulators, located one at each crew station, just above the right cockpit rail, automatically supply the required mixture and volume of oxygen. *(See figure 62.)*

d. A pressure gage (3) and signal lamp (2) are mounted adjacent to each regulator. They serve to indicate the amount of oxygen pressure available at each station and, when the system nears exhaustion, to signal the necessity of returning to a lower altitude where oxygen will not be required. *(See figure 62.)* The signal lamp is not installed on late P-61B airplanes.

e. A blinker flow indicator *(see 1, figure 62)* is mounted on the same panel with each pressure gage. The blinker flow indicator provides a visual indication that oxygen is being supplied.

f. **OPERATION.**

Note

The normal full pressure of the system is 425 lbs. Before take-off check to see that there is sufficient oxygen supply for the mission contemplated.

(1) Insert the male fitting of the mask (see that the gasket is in place) into the female end of the tubing from the regulator. Make sure that the fit is snug and that a pull of at least ten pounds is necessary to separate the two.

(2) AUTO-MIX CONTROL.—The normal position of the "AUTO-MIX" control is "ON." *(See 6, figure 62. In this position the regulator automat-

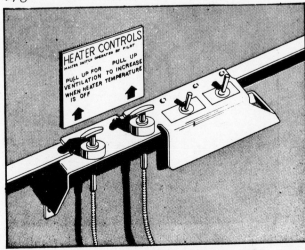

Figure 53 — Radio Operator's Heater Controls (P-61B)

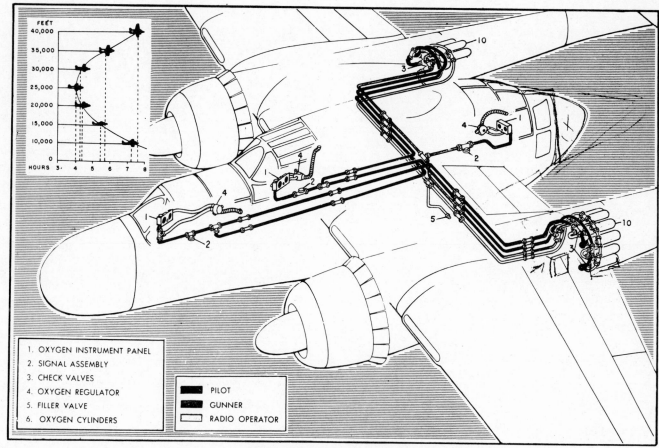

1. OXYGEN INSTRUMENT PANEL
2. SIGNAL ASSEMBLY
3. CHECK VALVES
4. OXYGEN REGULATOR
5. FILLER VALVE
6. OXYGEN CYLINDERS

▮ PILOT
▨ GUNNER
▯ RADIO OPERATOR

Figure 54 — Oxygen System

ically mixes the proper amount of air with the oxygen at all altitudes. When the "AUTO-MIX" control is in the "OFF" position the air port is closed. The regulator is still a demand regulator and will furnish **pure oxygen** on demand.

(3) EMERGENCY VALVE.—Turning the red knob marked "EMERGENCY" to "ON" converts the demand system to free flow and is an emergency device to be used only when the demand system fails. It is an extreme waste of oxygen to use it when it is not needed. *(See 4, figure 62.)*

g. PRECAUTIONS.

(1) In flight manipulate the mask at regular intervals when temperatures are low enough to cause ice formation in the mask.

(2) Use care to insure that the hose from the regulator to the mask does not become kinked, twisted, or disconnected.

(3) If a lack of oxygen is experienced, turn the red emergency knob on the regulator to "ON."

h. A pressure of 425 lbs. indicates a full oxygen system. This is approximately a five-hour supply for each member of the crew. *(See figure 54.)*

CAUTION

Extreme caution must be observed to insure

that oxygen equipment does not become contaminated with oil or grease. Fire or explosion may result when even slight traces of oil or grease come into contact with oxygen under pressure.

3. **COMMUNICATIONS EQUIPMENT.**
(See figure 55.)

a. **GENERAL DESCRIPTION.**—Provisions have been made for the installation of several complete sets of radio equipment, some of which are interchangeable as alternate installations.

(1) The pilot's radio push-button will operate whichever equipment is designated by the selector switch on Jack Box BC-366. *(See 7, figure 8.)*

(2) A three-way switch marked "INTERPHONE" is installed in the cover of the radio operator's microphone junction box. The three positions are "SPECIAL," "NORMAL," and "OFF." In the "SPECIAL" position, the "Tip" circuit of the foot switch is connected with the pilot's trigger switch. In the "NORMAL" position the "Tip" circuit of the floor switch is connected to plug PL-68 that plugs into the radio operator's BC-366 Jack Box. In this position the radio operator can operate any equipment he may select on BC-366 Jack

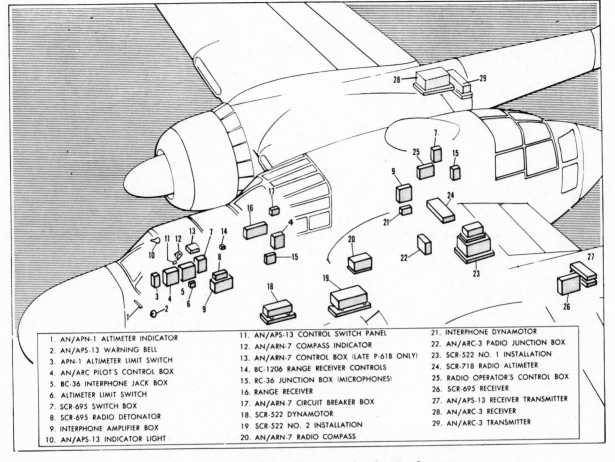

1. AN/APN-1 ALTIMETER INDICATOR	11. AN/APS-13 CONTROL SWITCH PANEL	21. INTERPHONE DYNAMOTOR
2. AN/APS-13 WARNING BELL	12. AN/ARN-7 COMPASS INDICATOR	22. AN/ARC-3 RADIO JUNCTION BOX
3. APN-1 ALTIMETER LIMIT SWITCH	13. AN/ARN-7 CONTROL BOX (LATE P-61B ONLY)	23. SCR-522 NO. 1 INSTALLATION
4. AN/ARC PILOT'S CONTROL BOX	14. BC-1206 RANGE RECEIVER CONTROLS	24. SCR-718 RADIO ALTIMETER
5. BC-36 INTERPHONE JACK BOX	15. RC-36 JUNCTION BOX (MICROPHONES)	25. RADIO OPERATOR'S CONTROL BOX
6. ALTIMETER LIMIT SWITCH	16. RANGE RECEIVER	26. SCR-695 RECEIVER
7. SCR-695 SWITCH BOX	17. AN/ARN-7 CIRCUIT BREAKER BOX	27. AN/APS-13 RECEIVER TRANSMITTER
8. SCR-695 RADIO DETONATOR	18. SCR-522 DYNAMOTOR	28. AN/ARC-3 RECEIVER
9. INTERPHONE AMPLIFIER BOX	19. SCR-522 NO. 2 INSTALLATION	29. AN/ARC-3 TRANSMITTER
10. AN/APS-13 INDICATOR LIGHT	20. AN/ARN-7 RADIO COMPASS	

Figure 55 — Radio and Communication Equipment

Box. (*See 13, figure 56.*) In the "OFF" position the "Tip" circuit to the microphone is open. The "OFF" position is required in order that the radio operator can use the combination interphone-side-tone facility of either SCR-522 set without turning on the transmitter (with selector switch in either "COMP" or "LIA" position).

b. **COMMAND SET.**—The airplane is equipped either with two sets of SCR-522-( ) or one set of AN/ARC-3. In addition, provisions are made for the installation of one set of SCR-274-N equipment.

(1) SCR-522-( ) EQUIPMENT.

(a) **LOCATION.**—The No. 1 set is installed on the left side of the radio operator's floor below the table. On P-61A and early P-61B airplanes the No. 2 set is installed between the two forward 20-mm cannon beneath the crew nacelle floor. On late P-61B airplanes the No. 2 set is located in the right-hand boom. The control boxes for both sets are located to the right of the pilot below the cockpit rail.

(b) **NORMAL OPERATION.**—All controls used in normal operation except the push-to-talk switch are located on the panel of the radio control box (BC-602-A). (*See 2, figure 55.*)

1. The five red push-buttons on the radio control box are the means by which channels are selected and power turned on or off. When the "OFF" button is depressed the dynamotor is stopped. The five push-buttons are so interconnected that not more than one can be in the depressed position at any given time.

2. The T-R-REM switch is wired fast in the "REM" position. In this position the transmitter-receiver control is transferred to a push-to-talk switch.

Note

Should the wire be broken or removed, the following conditions will prevail. In the "T" position the transmitter is placed in the continuous operation and in the "R" position the receiver is placed in continuous operation, providing one of the station selector buttons is depressed.

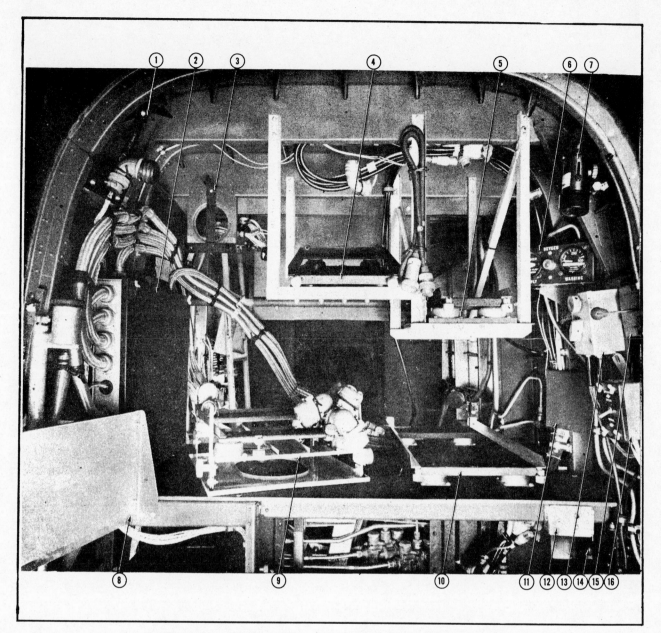

Figure 56 — Radio Operator's Compartment — Upper Front

1. MOUNTING FOR BC-1145-A CONTROL BOX
2. JB-98-A JUNCTION BOX
3. MOUNTING FOR RC-255-A RADIO CONTROL EQUIP.
4. MOUNTING FOR BC-929-A INDICATOR
5. MOUNTING FOR RA-88-A RECTIFIER
6. OXYGEN INSTRUMENTS
7. SPOTLIGHT
8. MOUNTING FOR BC-1150-A CONTROL BOX

9. MOUNTING FOR BC-1151-A RADIO OP. INDICATOR
10. MOUNTING FOR BC-1148-A SYNCHRONIZER
11. MOUNTING FOR SCR-274 RADIO
12. SPARE LAMP BOX
13. BC-366 INTERPHONE JACK BOX
14. SUIT HEAT RHEOSTAT
15. RADIO OPERATOR'S VENTILATOR
16. MICROPHONE SWITCH BOX

    3. Interphone communication is available at all times from the RC-36 interphone equipment.

(c) TRANSMISSION.

    1. To start the equipment press push-button "A," "B," "C," or "D," depending on the channel to be used.

    2. Allow approximately one minute for the vacuum tubes to warm up.

    3. Select the transmitter on BC-366 box.

    4. Depress the mike button.

    5. Speak into the microphone.

(d) RECEPTION.

    1. To start the equipment press button "A,' "B," "C," or "D."

    2. Select the receiver on BC-366 box.

Figure 57 — Radio Operator's Compartment — Lower Front

1. NO. 1 SCR-522 RADIO DYNAMOTOR
2. ALARM BELL
3. INTERPHONE JUNCTION BOX
4. SUIT HEAT RHEOSTAT

5. NO. 1 SCR-522 RADIO
6. RADIO JUNCTION BOX
7. INTERPHONE DYNAMOTOR
8. PUSH-TO-TALK SWITCH

9. EXTENSION LIGHT

(e) **PUSH-TO-TALK OPERATION.**

1. To start the equipment press button "A," "B," "C," or "D."

2. Under these conditions, the receiver is normally in operation.

3. To transmit, depress the push-to-talk switch and speak into the microphone.

(f) **STOPPING THE EQUIPMENT.** — To stop the equipment press the "OFF" button.

WARNING

Operation of this equipment involves the use of high voltages which are dangerous to life. Operating personnel must, at all times, observe all safety regulations. A dangerous potential exists on both the transmitter and receiver whenever the equipment is in either the transmit or receive condition.

(2) **AN/ARC-3 EQUIPMENT.**

(a) **LOCATION.**—The transmitter-receiver is installed in the right-hand tail boom. The control box is located to the right of the pilot below the cockpit rail.

(b) **OPERATION.**

1. **STARTING THE EQUIPMENT.** — Push any one of the eight red channel-selector buttons, designated "A" to "H," on the control box. This automatically releases the "OFF" button and applies power to the equipment.

c. **IDENTIFICATION EQUIPMENT.**

(1) Provisions have been made for the in-

stallation of SCR-695-( ) equipment for the identification of the airplane in flight.

(2) This equipment consists of a radio receiver, RC-255-A radio control equipment (see 3, figure 56) and a destructor unit.

(3) Radio control equipment RC-255-A, consisting of a power control box and a selector control box in mounted on a bracket near the left forward top corner of the radio operator's compartment, above the table.

(4) The pilot's remote controls for equipment SCR-695-( ) consist of four switches mounted on a bracket on the right of the pilot's cockpit. The 695 POWER switch is an ON-OFF toggle switch. The switch marked "EMERGENCY" is a remote emergency signal ON-OFF toggle switch. The other two switches are marked "695-G." One is an ON-OFF toggle switch for the G band operating mechanism and the other a push-button type ON-OFF switch for a time control of the G band. (See 17, figure 8.)

(5) OPERATION OF SCR-695-( ) EQUIPMENT.

(a) To start the equipment throw the ON-OFF switch on the RC-255-A control box or the pilot's remote control to "ON."

(b) Set the six-position switch on the selector control box to the position specified by the Communications Officer-in-Charge. In the absence of specific information, set the selector switch to position "1."

(c) Directions will be given as to the use of the G band switches.

(d) Details concerning the use of the emergency switch can be obtained from the Communications Officer-in-Charge.

(e) When the airplane is ready to take off, or preferably, as soon as it is in the air, insert the destructor plug in the destructor unit.

1. The destructor is designed to destroy radio receiver BC-966-( ) for reasons of secrecy should this become necessary while operating the airplane. The detonator is set off when a voltage of the required value or higher is placed across its terminals. This will occur if the inertia switch is operated or if the two buttons marked "DANGER" on switch box BC-765 are depressed simultaneously. (See 16, figure 8.)

2. When the airplane is on the ground for any length of time, the destructor plug should be disconnected from the destructor unit.

3. Always test the destructor circuit to make certain there is no voltage at the plug be-

fore attaching it to the destructor unit.

4. With the destructor plug removed and the inertia switch tripped the warning lights should light. With the inertia switch reset, the two DANGER buttons should be depressed simultaneously. Again the warning lights should light. After testing, set the switches including the inertia switch, for proper operating conditions as indicated by absence of light from the lamps. When teh inertia switch has been finally reset, its side should be rapped sharply with the knuckles. If correctly set, the switch should not be released thereby.

WARNING

The plug should never be inserted in the destructor when the warning lights are lighted.

(f) To stop the SCR-695-( ) equipment, throw all switches to the "OFF" position.

(g) Remove the destructor plug from the destructor unit as soon as the airplane lands in friendly territory.

d. INTERPHONE EQUIPMENT.—The RC-36 interphone system installed in the airplane provides intra-plane communication between the three crew stations, and includes switching facilities whereby the operation of the other radio equipment may be partially controlled. Controls for the system consist of a jack box mounted in each of the three crew compartments on the right-hand side, a push-to-talk switch on the floor of the radio operator's compartment, button switches on the left grip of each sighting station and on the throttle control, and a trigger switch on the left spoke of the pilot's control wheel.

(1) JACK BOX.—Each jack box consists essentially of a five-position selector switch and a volume control. The five switch positions are "COMMAND," "LIAISON," "INTER," "COMP," and "CALL.' The "INTER" position provides an intercommunication system between crew members. The "CALL" position connects a crew member with the other two interphone stations, regardless of the switch positions on the other jack boxes.

(2) OPERATION.—Voltage for the operation of the interphone amplifier is obtained from the dynamotor. There is no on-off switch in the interphone system, hence, the system is in operation whenever the master switch is "ON."

e. RADAR EQUIPMENT.—The SCR-720 equipment is mounted in the extreme nose of the airplane. Information concerning the operation of this equipment will be covered by separate documents available to the operating organization personnel. In addition to the SCR-720 equipment, P-61 airplanes are provided with SCR-729 radio equipment.

f. RADIO ALTIMETER. — P-61A and early P-61B airplanes are equipped with an SCR-718 raido altimeter. Late P-61B are provided with AN/APN-1 equipment.

(1) SCR-718 EQUIPMENT.—The equipment includes a transmitter-receiver, mounted below the radio operator's table, and an indicator, installed above and to the left of the radio operator's table. All controls for the equipment are located on the face of the indicator housing.

(a) TO START THE EQUIPMENT.—Turn the "REC. GAIN" control knob clockwise one-half turn. This should light the pilot light.

(b) TO STOP THE EQUIPMENT.—Turn the "REC. GAIN" control knob counterclockwise until the switch is opened.

(2) AN/APN-1 EQUIPMENT.—The equipment includes a transmitter-receiver mounted below the radio operator's table, a control panel *(see 6, figure 4)*, mounted above the automatic pilot pressure control, and an indicator *(see 9, figure 20)*, installed in the pilot's instrument panel.

(a) TO START THE EQUIPMENT.—Turn the "ALTITUDE LIMIT SWITCH," located on the control panel, clockwise, and allow the equipment to warm-up for one minute. As soon as the pointer on the indicator moves from its sub-zero position the equipment is functioning.

(b) TO STOP THE EQUIPMENT.—Turn the "ALTITUDE LIMIT SWITCH" to its extreme counterclockwise position.

g. AN/APS-13 RADIO.—This equipment is installed in all P-61 airplanes. The controls are on a panel mounted on the right-hand cockpit rail immediately above the pilot's radio controls. The warning bell is mounted below the anti-icer instrument panel and the ID-42/APS-13 indicator is mounted on a bracket attached to the side of the night binocular. *(See 6, figure 10.)*

(1) CONTROLS.—The controls consist of a "TEST" switch and an operating switch, both having "ON" and "OFF" positions, and a rheostat to control the intensity of the indicator light.

h. RADIO COMPASS.—A type MN-26C radio compass is installed in various P-61 airplanes. The control box, type MN-28C, is mounted on the cockpit rail to the right of the pilot. A type IN-4A indicator is mounted just forward of the control box. *(See 5 and 7, figure 4.)*

(1) CONTROLS.—The controls consist of a tuning crank, a band switch, a four position switch,

and three control knobs. The band switch provides for the selection of the three bands in association with the tuning dial. The four way switch has an "OFF" position, a "COMP" position, which provides compass operation; a "REC ANT." position and a 'REC LOOP" position, both of which permit the equipment to operate as a communication receiver. The "LIGHT" control knob regulates the brilliance of the lamp illuminating the calibrated dial. The "AUDIO" control knob regulates the level of the audio signal in the headset. The "COMPASS" control knob regulates the extent of pointer deflection of the indicator.

i. RANGE RECEIVER.—A BC-1206-A range receiver is located on the right side of the pilot's compartment on the cockpit rail above the generator control panel. The range receiver covers the frequency range from 200 to 400 KC (beacon and weather band). The manual volume control which incorporates the power switch, is mounted on the forward end of the receiver.

j. MICROPHONES.—Each crew member is provided with a variable sensitive throat microphone, T-30—( ) and headset HS-33.

Note

When a throat microphone is being used for either interphone or radio communication, it must be adjusted so that its two circular elements are held **snugly** against each side of the throat just above the Adam's apple. Speak **slowly**, DISTINCTLY, and in a **normal** tone of voice. Shouting will seriously distort the voice signal.

4. ICE ELIMINATING EQUIPMENT.

a. PROPELLER ANTI-ICER SYSTEM.

(1) DESCRIPTION. — Anti-icing equipment for the propellers includes a 6 US (5 Imperial) gallon tank with a built-in, electrically driven pump located beneath the floor just forward of the radio operator's entrance door, two spinners and slinger rings, and a rheostat control switch.

(2) CONTROLS.—The rheostat control switch and anti-icer fluid gage are located forward of the control column. *(See 5 and 6, figure 16.)*

b. WINDSHIELD DEFROSTER SYSTEM.

(1) P-61A.—A flexible tube held in a bracket on the right cockpit rail opposite the pilot's seat provides warm air for windshield defrosting. Air for this purpose comes from the pilot's cockpit heater which must be operating.

(2) P-61B.—Fixed defroster tubes are installed below the pilot's and gunner's windshields, and flexible defrosting tubes are installed at each of the three crew stations.

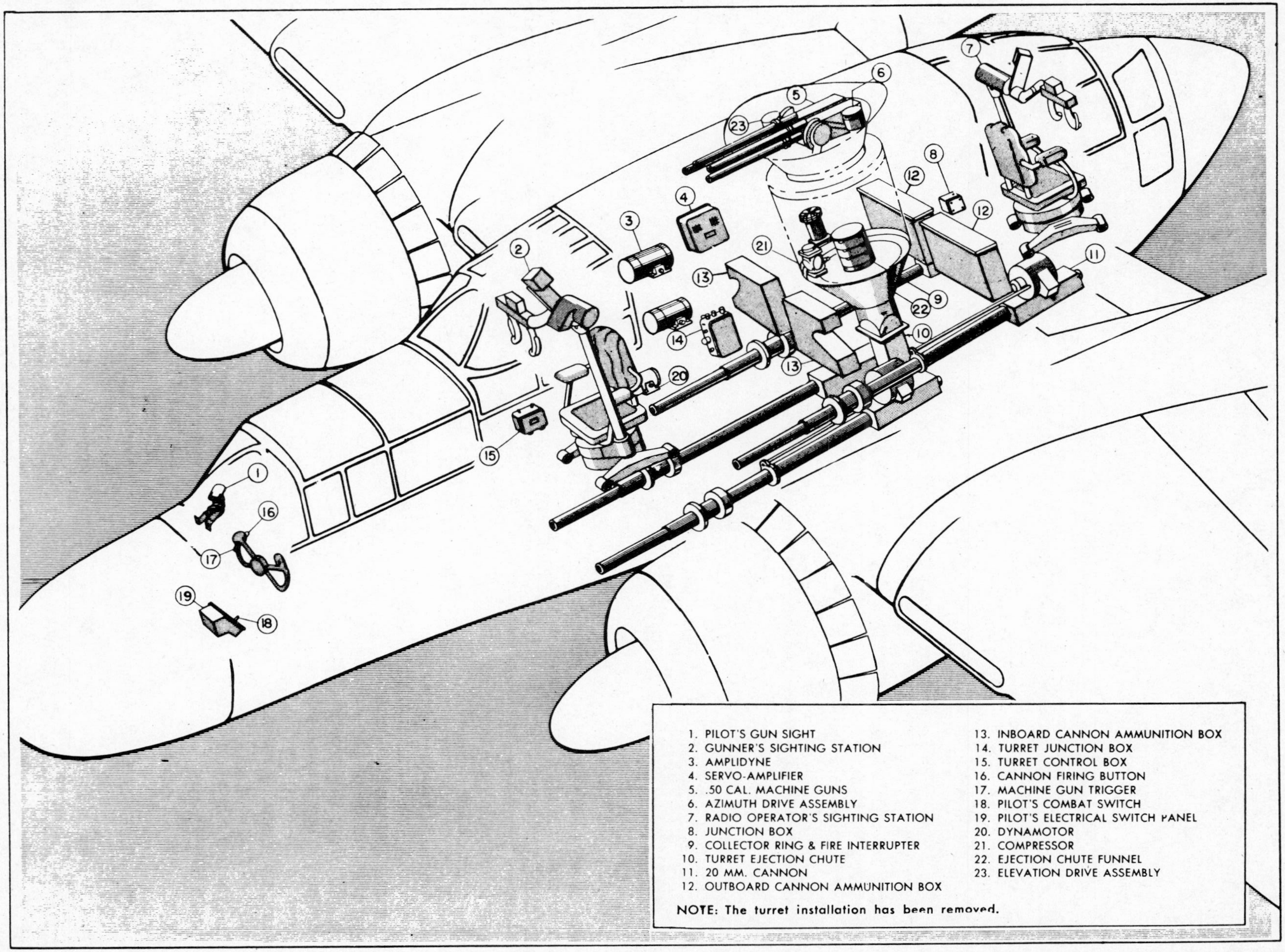

1. PILOT'S GUN SIGHT
2. GUNNER'S SIGHTING STATION
3. AMPLIDYNE
4. SERVO-AMPLIFIER
5. .50 CAL. MACHINE GUNS
6. AZIMUTH DRIVE ASSEMBLY
7. RADIO OPERATOR'S SIGHTING STATION
8. JUNCTION BOX
9. COLLECTOR RING & FIRE INTERRUPTER
10. TURRET EJECTION CHUTE
11. 20 MM. CANNON
12. OUTBOARD CANNON AMMUNITION BOX

13. INBOARD CANNON AMMUNITION BOX
14. TURRET JUNCTION BOX
15. TURRET CONTROL BOX
16. CANNON FIRING BUTTON
17. MACHINE GUN TRIGGER
18. PILOT'S COMBAT SWITCH
19. PILOT'S ELECTRICAL SWITCH PANEL
20. DYNAMOTOR
21. COMPRESSOR
22. EJECTION CHUTE FUNNEL
23. ELEVATION DRIVE ASSEMBLY

NOTE: The turret installation has been removed.

Figure 58—Gunnery Equipment.

3. GUNNER'S AND RADIO OPER-ATOR'S FLEXIBLE DEFROSTER. — Move the "CABIN AIR" lever on the anemostat to "OFF" and the "DEFROST" lever at the base of the tube to "ON." Use the tube as noted in paragraph *(b) 2*, preceding.

c. WING AND EMPENNAGE DE-ICER.

(1) DE-ICER BOOTS. — De-icer boots are provided for the leading edge of the outer wing and vertical and horizontal tail surfaces. Air for operation is supplied from the pressure side of both engine-driven vacuum pumps. The system is so designed that in event one pump fails, the other is sufficient to operate it.

(2) CONTROLS.—The de-icer control handle is located to the right of the pilot just below the cockpit rail. *(See 9, figure 8.)*

5. GUNNERY EQUIPMENT.

a. **20-MM CANNON.**—The airplane is equipped with four 20-mm fixed cannon, mounted on supports beneath the crew nacelle floor structure.

(1) CONTROLS.—Fire is controlled electrically by a firing switch button *(see 3, figure 13.)* mounted on the right side of the pilot's control wheel when the following switches are closed: the "CAMERA-COMBAT" switch on the pilot's electrical switch panel *(see 11, figure 24)* ("COMBAT" position), the pilot's gunsight circuit breaker switch on the aft main switch panel in the turret compartment, the cannon relay switch on the generator control panel *(see 15, figure 44)*, and both micro switches which are actuated when the nose gear doors are closed.

(2) AMMUNITION.—Each cannon is provided with a 200 round ammunition box. The outboard cannon ammunition boxes, reached through doors on the outside of the crew nacelle, are accessible only from the ground. The inboard cannon ammunition boxes are located behind the front wing spar on the crew nacelle floor and are accessible from the gunner's compartment. The cannon are charged manually on the ground. If one or more of the cannon should jam, the others will continue to operate.

CAUTION

The pilot should not place the CAMERA-COMBAT switch in the "Combat" position until he is ready to fire. The switch must be in the "Off" position before landing the airplane.

b. **PILOT'S GUN SIGHT.**—On P-61A airplanes the pilot is provided with a Type L-1 gun sight mounted on the coaming above the instrument

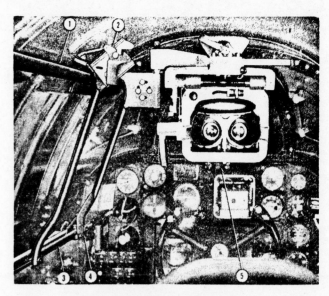

Figure 59 — Night Binocular

1. UPPER TRACK
2. STOWED POSITION LATCH
3. LOWER TRACK
4. CARRIAGE RELEASE
5. NIGHT BINOCULAR

panel. On P-61B airplanes a Type LY-3N sight is installed. The sight lamp is operated by a switch located on the right side of the gun sight and controlled by a rheostat mounted on the pilot's electrical panel.

c. **NIGHT BINOCULARS.**—A night binocular is mounted on an arm which permits it to swing into place aft of the pilot's armor glass. It stows at the left of the gunner's armor glass by sliding aft on track mounted on the cockpit rail. *(See figure 59.)*

d. **FLEXIBLE GUNS.**

Note

The turret installation has been removed.

(1) TURRET.—A rotatable turret mounting four .50 caliber machine guns is provided on early P-61A and late P-61B airplanes. The guns fire simultaneously at a rate of approximately 800 rounds per minute. The turret has full 360° rotation in azimuth and the guns can be elevated 90° from horizontal. *(See figure 60.)* The movement of the turret and guns is electrically controlled from two sighting stations located forward and aft of the turret in the gunner's and radio operator's compartments respectively. The gunner, radio operator, or pilot can control the firing of the guns. The gunner has full control of the turret at all times unless he chooses to transfer control to the radio operator. On early P-61A airplanes, the gunner may transfer control to the pilot by rotating the turret, pointing the guns in a forward position, and turning "OFF" the "TURRET POWER" switch. *(See 15, figure 62.)* When this switch is "OFF," the stowing latch drops down and latches

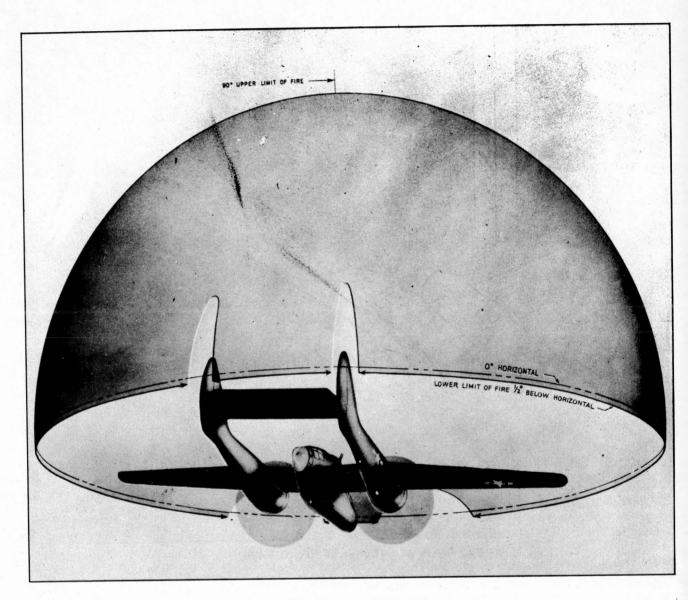

Figure 60 — Cones of Fire (Turret)

the turret. The gunner must then throw the "FIRE SELECTOR" switch *(see 13, figure 62)* to the "PILOT" firing position. On late P-61B airplanes, the turret automatically returns to the strafing position when the action switches on all sighting-arm grips are open. (See paragraph 5 **d** **(4)** **(h)**, following.) Each machine gun is provided with an ammunition case with a maximum capacity of approximately 560 rounds of ammunition.

(2) SIGHTING STATIONS. *(See 13, figure 63.)* The sighting station consists primarily of a seat assembly, a rotating housing which mounts a support column, which in turn supports the sighting arm, all of which are supported by a base mounted on a track.

(3) CONTROLS.

(a) TURRET CONTROL BOX. *(See figure 62.)*—The turret control box is mounted below the right cockpit rail opposite the forward gunner's position. The "A-C POWER" switch (12) controls the dynamotor and the "TURRET POWER" switch (15) controls the amplidyne motor generators. The "CAMERA" switch (16) is provided to control a turret camera which can be installed in the turret. These three switches have "ON" and "OFF" positions. A fourth switch, the "FIRE SELECTOR" switch (13), transfers firing control from the gunner to the pilot. It has three positions; "GUNNER," "SAFE," and "PILOT." The control box also contains three push-button type circuit breakers, one on the top and two on the forward end.

(b) SIGHTING STATION. *(See figure 64.)* Firing controls at the sighting station are mounted

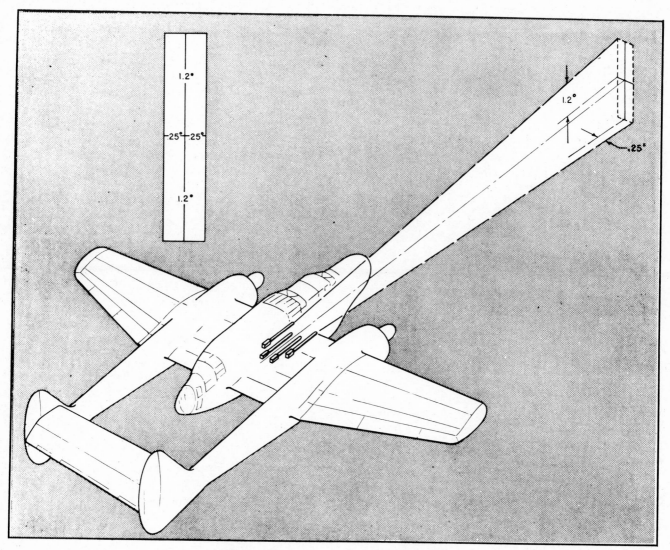

Figure 61 — Cones of Fire (Cannon)

on the two grips attached to the sighting arm. Each grip contains a hand grip action switch (6 and 8) and a trigger switch. The trigger switch is mounted on the front of the grip away from the operator. All four turret guns are fired by any trigger. The hand grip action switches are mounted on the outboard side of the grips. They are depressed by the palm of the hand and pressure on either or both provides complete control over the turret. (The button switch (9) on the left grip provides interphone connection.)

(4) OPERATION OF THE TURRET FIRE CONTROL SYSTEM.

(a) Immediately after take-off, place the "A-C POWER" switch in the "ON" position and leave it there until just before landing. This permits the system to warm up and the air compressor to build up pressure, insuring proper operation of the guns throughout the entire period of the mission.

(b) Unstow the sighting station in elevation by pulling out the elevation stowage pin and lowering the sighting arm to the desired position. Unstow the sighting station in azimuth by pulling out on the azimuth stowage knob and turning it to fix the lock in the unstowed position.

(c) Place the "TURRET POWER" switch in the "ON" position to energize the azimuth and elevation amplidyne generators. This is not necessary until operation of the turret and sighting stations is required and, in any case, should not be accomplished until 30 seconds after the "A-C POWER" circuit has been closed.

(d) If the turret is to be operated by the gunner or radio operator, place the "FIRE SELECTOR" switch in the "GUNNER" position.

CAUTION

The fire selector switch should always be returned to the "SAFE" position when the system is not in use.

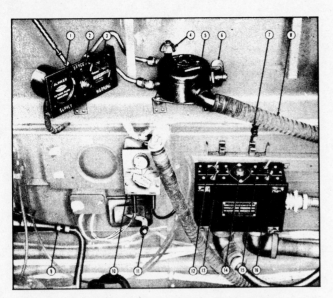

Figure 62 — Gunner's Compartment — Right Side

1. OXYGEN FLOW INDICATOR
2. OXYGEN WARNING LIGHT (NOT ON LATE P-61B)
3. OXYGEN PRESSURE GAGE
4. EMERGENCY VALVE CONTROL
5. FLEXIBLE TUBE CONNECTOR
6. AUTO-MIX CONTROL
7. PEN LIGHT BRACKET
8. FLEXIBLE OXYGEN TUBE
9. RELIEF TUBE
10. RADIO JACK BOX
11. GUNNER'S VENTILATOR
12. A-C POWER SWITCH
13. POWER SELECTOR SWITCH
14. CIRCUIT BREAKER
15. TURRET POWER SWITCH
16. CAMERA SWITCH

(e) Depress the hand-grip action-switch on the sighting-arm grip to control the turret. The gunner's sighting station has primary control and the radio operator can control the turret only when the gunner's action switches are open.

(f) To fire the turret guns, depress the trigger switch on either sighting arm grip.

(g) On early P-61A airplanes, to give control to the pilot, lock the turret guns in the straight ahead position. Place the "FIRE SELECTOR" switch in the "PILOT" position. Fire the turret guns by pressing the trigger switch on the right side of the control wheel. *(See 4, figure 13.)*

(h) On late P-61B airplanes, if the turret is to be controlled by the pilot, the gunner and radio operator must open all action switches. The turret will automatically return to the strafing position. Leave the "A-C POWER" and "TURRET POWER" switches "ON." Place the "FIRE SELECTOR" switch in the "PILOT" position. To fire the turret guns, press the trigger switch on the right side of the control wheel.

(5) ADJUSTMENTS.

(a) **HEIGHT ADJUSTMENT.**—To adjust the sight to the required eye level of the individual gunner, loosen the locking wheel near the top of the support column and turn the adjusting wheel until the desired position is obtained. Tighten the locking wheel. *(See 13, figure 64.)*

(b) **DISTANCE ADJUSTMENT.**—To adjust the sight to the proper distance from the eye of the gunner, loosen the set screw (3) and adjusting nut (10) on the flange and tube assembly of the elevation arm. This permits the sighting arm to move in and out. When the desired adjustment is obtained, tighten the set screw and adjusting nut. *(See figure 64.)*

(6) MOVING THE SIGHTING STATION.

Note

The gunner's sighting station normally should not be moved on the track during flight.

(a) On early P-61A airplanes, to move the sighting station fore and aft, pull up and turn the locking knobs, one of which is located on each leg. On late P-61B airplanes, lift up the locking bolt handle at the front of the base. The sighting station will now roll on the track within the limits of the track bumpers. The gunner's sighting station locks in the firing position only. The radio operator's sighting station can be locked in either the firing or radio operating positions.

(b) To rotate the housing and elevation arm, pull out the stowage locking knob and turn it 180°. The sight may now be rotated through 350°.

(c) To rotate the seat only, lift up the lever on the left side of the seat pan and place it in a latched position. The seat is now free to rotate through 360°. Release the lever to unlatch and move the seat until it snaps into a locked position (0° or 180°)

Note

Normally it will not be necessary to move the seat during flight.

(7) STOWING THE SIGHT.

CAUTION

Place the "A-C POWER" switch and the "TURRET POWER" switch in the "OFF" position before stowing the sight.

(a) To place the elevation unit in its stowed position, lift the elevation arm until the stowage pin passes the stop and snaps into the locking clip.

5. EXTERNAL WING RACKS. *(See figure 66.)*

   a. **DESCRIPTION.** — Provisions are made on late P-61A and early P-61B airplanes for the installation of two external droppable fuel tanks chemical tanks, or bombs. One installation is made under each outer wing. Late P-61B airplanes are equipped for the installation of external, droppable items under both the inner and outer wings.

   b. **CONTROLS.** — (Airplanes with outer wing racks only.) *(See figure 65.)*

   (1) **DESCRIPTION.** — On airplanes with outer wing racks only the bomb selector controls are

   (b) To stow the azimuth unit, rotate the housing to approximately zero degrees azimuth position and turn the stowage locking knobs 180° to the released position. If the locking pin does not snap into the keeper, rotate the housing slowly back and forth until it locks.

   (8) **GUN SIGHTS.** — Each sighting arm mounts a Type N-6 gun sight. The two filaments of the gun sight lamp may be selected by a switch on the left side of the sight. The lamp is adjusted by turning the rheostat on the support arm until the desired intensity of light is obtained.

Figure 63A — Gunner's Compartment (P-61B)

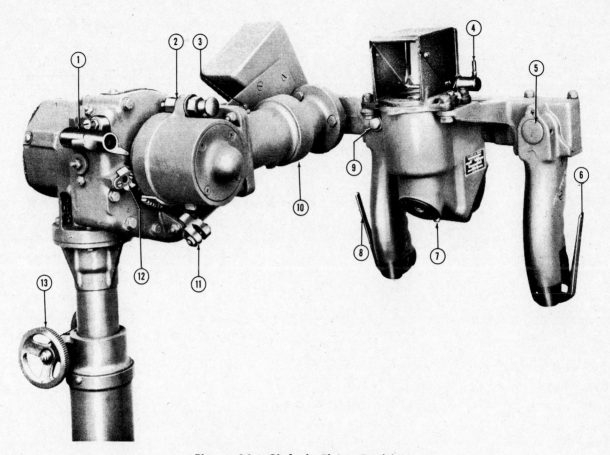

Figure 64 — Sight in Firing Position

mounted on the right cockpit rail, opposite the pilot. They consist of two selector switches and one salvo switch. The bomb selector switches are provided with three positions, "OFF," "BOMBS ARMED," and "CHEM TANKS." A push-button type switch, marked "TANK — RELEASE — BOMBS," is mounted on the upper right spoke of the control wheel and provides the actual release control. A switch type circuit breaker, marked "BOMB CONTROL," and a push-button type circuit breaker, marked "SALVO," for the salvo circuit are located on the generator control panel.

(2) OPERATION.

(a) **TO RELEASE BOMBS ARMED.**

1. On generator control panel, switch "ON" circuit breaker marked "BOMB CONTROL."

2. On bomb selector switch panel, turn switch corresponding to the desired bomb to "BOMBS ARMED" position.

3. Press the release button on the control wheel.

(b) **TO RELEASE BOMBS SAFE.**—Bomb┃ can only be released safe on the salvo circuit. Se┃ paragraph *(e)*, following.

(c) **TO RELEASE CHEMICALS FROM┃ CHEMICAL TANKS.**

1. On generator control panel, switc┃ "ON" circuit breaker marked "BOMB CONTROL.┃

2. On bomb selector switch panel, tur┃ switch corresponding to the desired tank t┃ "CHEM TANKS." Chemicals will be released in┃ mediately as the switch is actuated.

(d) **TO RELEASE CHEMICAL TANKS.**┃ Follow the procedure described in *(a)*, preceding┃

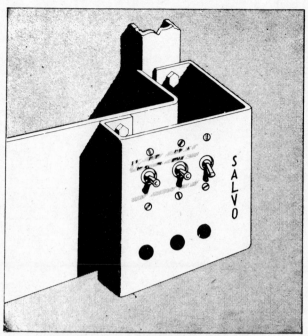

**Figure 65 — Bomb Release Controls
(Two Shackle Installation)**

if chemicals have been spent and it is desired to release tanks individually. Otherwise, use "SALVO" as described in *(e)*, following.

(e) **TO RELEASE UNITS BY "SALVO."**—On the bomb selector switch panel, raise the handle marked "SALVO." Units on both shackles will leave the airplane simultaneously as the handle is raised. The circuit breaker marked "SALVO" on the generator control panel is normally on at all times.

Note

The salvo operation will release bombs in the safe condition and drop chemical tanks without releasing the chemicals.

c. **CONTROLS.**—(Intermediate P-61B airplanes.) *(See figure 21.)*

(1) DESCRIPTION.—On intermediate P-61B airplanes the bomb selector switch panel is mounted below the right cockpit rail. It contains four, three position switches, one for each droppable installation. The three positions are "OFF," "SAFE," and "ARM." There is no salvo circuit. A push-button type switch on the upper right spoke of the control wheel provides the release control. A switch type circuit breaker marked "BOMB CONTROL" is located on the generator control box. The chemical tank selector switch panel is located below the right cockpit rail. It contains four switches, one for each tank, each with an "OFF" position and an "ON" position designated by the name of the tank.

(2) OPERATION.

(a) **TO RELEASE BOMBS ARMED.**

1. On the generator control panel, switch "ON" circuit breaker marked "BOMB CONTROL."

2. On bomb selector switch panel, turn the switch corresponding to the desired bomb to "ARM."

3. Press the release button on the control wheel.

(b) **TO RELEASE BOMBS SAFE.**

1. Follow the procedure in *(a)*, except, in step 2, place the switch in the "SAFE" position.

(c) **TO RELEASE CHEMICALS FROM CHEMICAL TANKS.**

1. On generator control panel, switch "ON" circuit breaker marked "BOMB CONTROL."

2. Note that all switches on bomb selector switch panel are "OFF."

3. On chemical tank selector switch panel, turn the switch corresponding to the desired tank on.

4. Press the release button on the control wheel.

(d) **TO RELEASE CHEMICAL TANKS FROM AIRPLANE.**—Follow the procedure in *(a)*, preceding, except, in step 2, place the bomb selector switch corresponding to the chemical tank to be released in the "SAFE" position.

(e) **TO RELEASE UNITS BY SALVO.**—Follow the procedure described in *(a)*, preceding, except that all four switches on the bomb selector switch panel must be turned to "SAFE."

d. **CONTROLS.**—(Late P-61B airplanes.)
(See figure 22.)

(1) DESCRIPTION.—The bomb selector switch panel is mounted on the right cockpit rail, opposite the pilot. The panel contains six switches and four indicator lights. Each shackle is controlled by an individual two-way switch with a "SAFE" position and an on position marked "CHEM—ARM—TANK." Each of these switches is protected by a guard against accidental release. An indicator light, mounted above the control switch for each shackle, turns on when the switch is in the on position and the unit has not been released from the shackle. The other two switches, marked "SALVO" are linked together and controlled by a single handle.

(2) OPERATION.

(a) **TO RELEASE BOMBS ARMED.**

1. On generator control panel, switch "ON" circuit breaker marked "BOMB CONTROL."

2. On bomb selector switch panel, turn switch corresponding to desired bomb to "ARM."

Immediately, as the selector switch is displaced from "OFF," the indicator light for the selected station will go on.

3. Press the release button on the control wheel. As soon as the bomb has left the airplane, the indicator light will go out, indicating that the bomb has cleared the shackle.

(b) TO RELEASE BOMBS SAFE.—Follow the procedure in *(a)* except, in step 2, place the selector switch in the "SAFE" position.

(c) TO RELEASE CHEMICALS FROM CHEMICAL TANKS.

1. On generator control panel, switch "ON" circuit breaker marked "BOMB CONTROL."

2. On bomb selector switch panel, turn the switch corresponding to the desired tank to "CHEM." Immediately, as the switch is displaced from "OFF," the chemicals will be released from the tank and the indicator light for the selected station will go on. The indicator light will remain on until either the selector switch is returned to "OFF" or the release button on the control is pressed. When the light goes out it indicates that the bomb has cleared the shackle.

(d) TO RELEASE UNITS BY "SALVO."

1. On the generator control panel, switch "ON" the circuit breaker marked "BOMB CONTROL."

2. On the bomb selector switch panel, turn the handle marked "SALVO" up. Immediately as the switch is displaced, the indicator lights for all stations will go on.

3. Press the release button on the control wheel. As soon as the units leave the airplane the indicator lights will go out.

4. Later P-61B airplanes also have mechanical release at left of pilot.

Note

Indicator lights remaining on after the release button has been pressed show that the units at the stations indicated have not left the shackle as they should.

7. PHOTOGRAPHIC EQUIPMENT.

a. DESCRIPTION. — An electrically operated camera which works in conjunction with the cannon, is installed in the crew nacelle nose. The camera operates for the length of time the pilot's cannon trigger *(see 3, figure 13)* is depressed, plus the time for which the overrun control is set.

d. CONTROLS.—The operational controls consist of a switch mounted on the pilot's electrical switch panel. *(See 11, figure 24.)* The switch has three positions; "OFF," "CAMERA," and "COMBAT." The "COMBAT" position permits operation of both the cannon and camera. The "CAMERA" position provides for operation of the camera alone. When the equipment is not in use the switch must be placed in the "OFF" position.

c. OPERATION.

(1) Place switch on pilot's electrical switch panel in "COMBAT" position if the camera is to be used in connection with the cannon. Place switch in "CAMERA" position if camera is to be used alone.

(2) Depress the 20-mm cannon switch on the control wheel.

(3) Return the switch on the pilot's electrical switch panel to "OFF" when the operation is completed.

8. MISCELLANEOUS EQUIPMENT.

a. PILOT'S SEAT.—The P-61A airplanes are equipped with a pilot's seat which is mounted on tracks and rollers. The P-61B airplanes are provided with a pilot's seat which is bolted to the floor.

(1) ADJUSTMENTS OF PILOT'S SEAT.

(a) The upper aft control lever located on the right side of the pilot's seat allows the seat to be raised by an elastic shock cord or lowered by the weight of the pilot. The lower forward control lever at the right side of the pilot's seat allows the seat pan to be tilted up or down.

(b) The complete seat can be tilted back to facilitate entrance and exit. The seat is released for tilting by pressing down the knob located on the back of the seat at the top and to the right of the center.

(c) In addiion to the above adjustments, the pilot's seat in the P-61A airplanes may be moved to the right of center on its track for easier entrance and exit. The track adjustment lever is located below the seat on the left side.

b. RADIO OPERATOR'S SEAT. (Late P-61A and early P-61B airplanes.)

(1) DESCRIPTION. — The radio operator's seat is mounted on a post assembly which is held in the seat base by a locking pin. The locking pin is operated by a lever on the left-hand side of the seat directly under the arm rest.

(2) MOVING THE SEAT.—See paragraph **5 *d*** (6) in this Section.

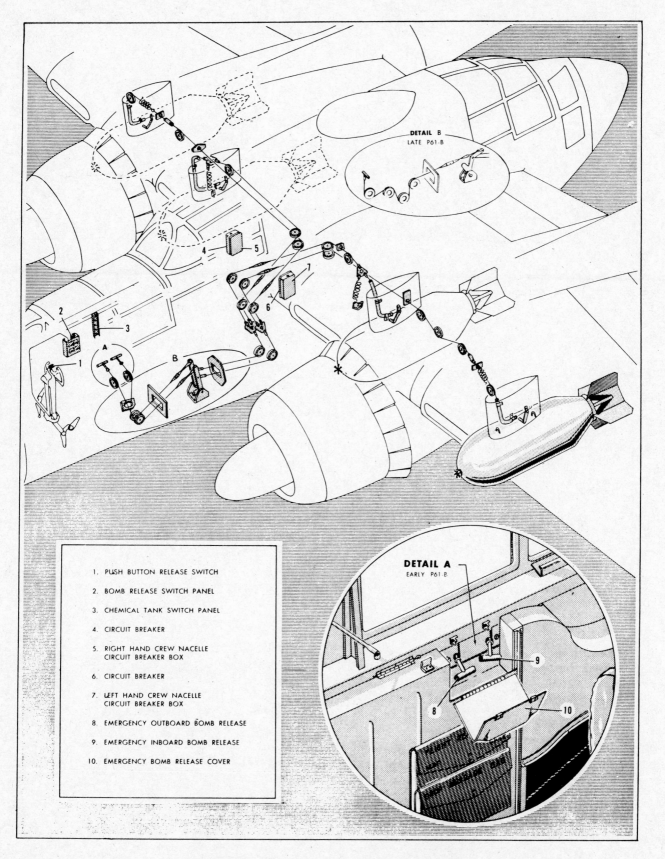

DETAIL B
LATE P-61-B

DETAIL A
EARLY P-61-B

1. PUSH BUTTON RELEASE SWITCH

2. BOMB RELEASE SWITCH PANEL

3. CHEMICAL TANK SWITCH PANEL

4. CIRCUIT BREAKER

5. RIGHT HAND CREW NACELLE
   CIRCUIT BREAKER BOX

6. CIRCUIT BREAKER

7. LEFT HAND CREW NACELLE
   CIRCUIT BREAKER BOX

8. EMERGENCY OUTBOARD BOMB RELEASE

9. EMERGENCY INBOARD BOMB RELEASE

10. EMERGENCY BOMB RELEASE COVER

Figure 66 — External Armament Control System

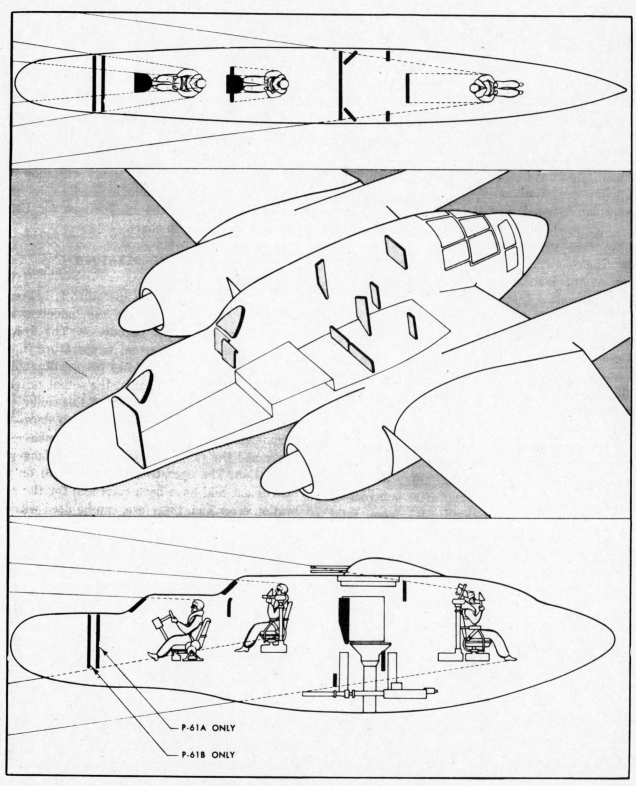

P-61A ONLY

P-61B ONLY

Figure 67 — Angles of Armor Protection

Viewed from the top, the *Black Widow* exhibits it unique spoilers in place of conventional ailerons.